D0722361

COME AS YOU ARE

First presented at the New Theatre in 1970, with Glynis Johns, Denholm Elliot, Joss Ackland and Pauline Collins, *Come As You Are* is a sequence of four one-act plays. Irving Wardle in *The Times* called it 'a sex comedy worthy of the name . . . that catches its characters at the moment they realize they are beginning to go off, and extracts its fun from the fact that they no longer know exactly who they are or what they can do.' *Come As You Are* shows Mortimer in top form as a master of the one-act play. It offers brilliant opportunities for a cast of four to display their versatility in a whole range of moods from sombre pathos to high farce.

The photograph on the front of the cover shows Glynis Johns in 'Marble Arch' in the original London production; photo Reg Wilson. The photograph on the back of the cover is reproduced by courtesy of the Radio Times.

COME AS YOU ARE

BY

John C. Mortimer

METHUEN & CO LTD
11 NEW FETTER LANE · LONDON EC4

First published 1971
© *1971 by Advanpress Ltd*
Printed in Great Britain by
Cox & Wyman Ltd
Fakenham, Norfolk
SBN 416 63270 x/24 Hardbound
416 63280 7/24 Paperback

Contents

The plays were first produced at the New Theatre, London, on January 27, 1970 with the following casts:

Mill Hill:

DENISE BLUNDELL	*Glynis Johns*
PETER TRILBY	*Denholm Elliot*
ROY BLUNDELL	*Joss Ackland*

Bermondsey:

IRIS PURVIS	*Glynis Johns*
BOB PURVIS	*Joss Ackland*
PIP LESTER	*Denholm Elliot*
ROSEMARY	*Pauline Collins*

Gloucester Road:

BUNNY THOMPSON	*Glynis Johns*
MIKE THOMPSON	*Denholm Elliot*
TOBY DELGARDO	*Joss Ackland*
CLARE DOBSON	*Pauline Collins*

Marble Arch:

LAURA LOGAN	*Glynis Johns*
MCNEE	*Joss Ackland*
MISS PARKER	*Pauline Collins*
MAX	*Denholm Elliot*

Director: Allan Davis
Designer: Alan Tagg

Mill Hill

Characters

DENISE BLUNDELL

PETER TRILBY

ROY BLUNDELL

The bedroom of a house in Mill Hill, an afternoon in summer.

A bedroom (furnished in Heals contemporary) in ROY BLUNDELL'S *house in Mill Hill: the home of a prosperous Harley Street dentist. There is a big covered bed, stage left. Right, an armchair and a dressing-table with a mirror. Upstage centre, the door to the landing. Right, the door to the bathroom. The stage is empty as the curtain rises, bright sunshine pouring through the window. It is 2.30 in the afternoon. The door to the landing opens cautiously,* DENISE BLUNDELL *comes in furtively, looks around, goes to the window and draws the curtains, shutting out the light of day. She is blonde, attractive, late twenties, dressed for a lunch out. After she has drawn the curtains she turns to the open door.*

DENISE. Roy? Roy? (*Whispers.*) All right, Peter, come in. No one's at home.

PETER TRILBY *appears at the door wearing a grey pin-striped suit and soft suède shoes. He is carrying a rather long and narrow suitcase.*

PETER (*whispers*). Are you sure the coast's clear?
DENISE (*whispers*). Absolutely clear. (*She switches on all the lights at the door so that the room is now brightly lit.*)
PETER. Your husband must be doing very nicely up in Harley Street, skimming the cream. (*He puts the suitcase down on the bed. Looks round the room.*) Why are we whispering?
DENISE (*she moves towards him, her voice full of love*). Peter . . . Darling.
PETER. I bet he double crowns some of the best-fed teeth in the country. (*He smiles and puts his arms round her.*) We've got the whole afternoon.

DENISE. Isn't it marvellous? (*She squints down at the clock by the bed.*) Of course, I've got to fetch Gerald from school ...

He sits down on the bed, discouraged, beside his suitcase.

PETER (*displeased*). What time do they let young Gerald out?

DENISE. Four-thirty ... We've got two hours.

PETER. Two hours, eh! I suppose that might be enough. (*He looks at his watch.*) No chance of Gerald being kept in or anything? (*Hopefully.*) I mean, he might have made a pig's breakfast of his Latin Prose.

DENISE. Gerald doesn't do Latin.

PETER. Pity ...

DENISE. He is only five.

PETER. Oh, well. Two hours'll have to do, then ...

He gets up, wanders round the room. She takes off her coat, hangs it in the cupboard.

DENISE. It's the first time – we've had – to be alone.

PETER. I get so little time off from the surgery ...

DENISE. Of course, it's been lovely just having lunch ... They must think we're married at the Trattoria in Cricklewood Road.

PETER. National Health stoppings for endless *au pair* girls! Never get a decent heterogenous dental transplant like your old man ...

DENISE. Please try to forget about teeth for a moment, darling ... (*She comes back towards him from the cupboard.*) Do you feel incredibly romantic ...?

PETER (*doing his best*). Incredibly ...

Long pause. They are both at a loss.

DENISE. Would you like a cigarette?

PETER. No thanks.

DENISE. Drink, or anything?

PETER. No, really ...

She lights a cigarette. Then goes to a cassette music player by the bed.

DENISE. Peter. You love music, don't you?

PETER. Within reason.

She puts a cassette into the machine. A Musak type rendering of 'The more I see you . . .'

DENISE. You remember . . . ? The first time we set eyes on each other . . . ?

PETER. Of course. (*Pause.*) When was it?

DENISE. It was the music in the lift going up for the London Dental Association's annual do . . .

They move towards each other : start to dance formally.

PETER. I quite forgot what the lift was playing . . .

DENISE. I wanted to dance with you there and then!

PETER. Oh, so did I . . . I couldn't believe my luck! I got your 'phone number out of you when your husband wasn't looking.

DENISE. We didn't come here just to talk about Roy, did we?

The music stops abruptly. They move away from each other.

DENISE. Do you want me to undress, Peter?

PETER (*firmly*). No. No. Not exactly.

DENISE (*puzzled*). Then what . . . ?

PETER. I don't actually want you to undress . . .

DENISE. We needn't be shy.

She sits down on the bed, holds his hand. He breaks away from her, moves about the room.

PETER. I am . . . shy by nature. Shy and reserved. I carry with me something rather unusual . . . (*He looks at the suitcase on the bed beside her.*)

DENISE (*looking at him*). You're an unusual person, Peter.

PETER. Up to now I haven't had the courage to open up . . . the subject.

DENISE. Open it up now!

Pause. He thinks of a new approach.

PETER. You do come from a medical household . . .

DENISE (*gets up, goes to him*). What is it, Peter? I'm really dying to know.

PETER. Have you browsed at all, through the standard works on sexual deviation?

DENISE (*shakes her head*). I trained as a Dental Nurse . . .

PETER. Oh. This is something which the late Professor Kraft-Ebbing apparently never stumbled on. In all his wide experience!

DENISE. Tell me what you want, Peter!

PETER. It's rather awkward . . .

DENISE. It doesn't matter – you'll find me deft and quite athletic . . .

PETER. Athletic . . . ?

DENISE. We had a craze for Judo – in my last year at the Hendon High.

PETER. Judo, actually, won't be necessary . . . We become attached to things, apparently in early childhood – so the Great Professor taught us.

DENISE. Kraft – what-not?

PETER. Freud.

DENISE. You seem to know an awful lot of Professors . . .

PETER. In a way I became attached to this, at the age of thirteen.

DENISE. You were interfered with . . .

PETER. Spiritually . . . in a history lesson.

DENISE. History!

PETER. A Mr Bulstrode, a small fat man with a ginger moustache was talking, as I remember, one far-off hot afternoon about the late Tudors . . .

DENISE (*incredulous*). The late Tudors?

PETER. Their effect on our history. As I recall it he spoke to us of Sir Francis Drake and the 'Golden Hind', Bacon's essays and singeing the King of Spain's beard.

DENISE. His beard?

PETER. His beard. When the little English frigates came dancing into Cadiz harbour scattering cannon balls like flowers on a fine May morning . . .

DENISE. Peter. Peter darling. I don't want to seem impatient . . . (*She moves towards the bed.*)

PETER. Bulstrode was, as I remember it clearly, droning on about the French alliance, the Low Countries and the Protestant succession. My attention wandered . . .

DENISE (*yawns*). I'm not surprised.

PETER. And then he suddenly said it.

DENISE. What?

PETER. Sir Walter Raleigh!

DENISE (*unimpressed*). Oh.

PETER (*anxious*). Well?

DENISE. He said 'Sir Walter Raleigh' . . .

PETER. Doesn't it mean much to you? I know . . . some people don't care about him at all. I have to face up to that.

DENISE. Oh yes. (*She goes to the mirror. Looks at herself, now a little anxiously.*) Sir Walter Raleigh. Of course. You mean the fellow with the tobacco?

PETER. Not the tobacco! (*Very serious and impressive.*) The cloak.

DENISE. Oh yes . . . Yes, of course. The cloak.

PETER. I suppose you think it's just something I picked up at my public school.

DENISE. Well, I know you men do acquire odd things, with your education . . .

PETER. When I heard about that cloak, young as I was, the world seemed lit by a curious and vivid glow . . . my hands were wet and I gulped for air. I clutched the edge of my seat because I felt in great danger of falling. I promised myself that when I grew up, and if I met a woman who really cared . . .

He moves quickly away from her, goes to the suitcase. Takes off his jacket and puts the case flat on the bed.

DENISE. Peter! You had that with you at lunchtime.

PETER. And always on these occasions. Don't laugh.

DENISE. You put it in the cloakroom of the Trattoria Michael-angelo and after lunch, it came with us in the car.

PETER. You're laughing!

DENISE. I'm not ...

He opens the suitcase quickly, brings out a hat like Sir Walter Raleigh's. He puts it on, then looks at her anxiously.

PETER. Well. What do you think?

DENISE (*utterly at a loss*). It's very nice, Peter. Very nice indeed.

PETER (*he brings out a sword, buckles it on quickly*). The sword goes with it ... of course and this! (*He brings out a velvet cloak with a white ruff stitched to the collar, so that when he does up the cloak, it looks as if he had the ruff on underneath it.*) This is a bit of a cheat actually.

DENISE. Really?

PETER. I had the ruff sewn on. It makes it easier – to get on and off in a hurry.

DENISE. I see ...

PETER. Well, for heaven's sake, Denise. We can't all be dead straight up and down.

DENISE. I accept that.

PETER. Good.

DENISE. I'm prepared to accept that totally ...

PETER. I thought you would.

DENISE. Why? Why did you think I would?

PETER. You can usually tell ... (*He looks at his watch.*) We shan't be long now. Here's yours. (*Quickly hands her a long jewelled Elizabethan dress.*)

DENISE. What on earth ... ?

PETER. The pearls aren't real, I'm afraid. In fact, I had it run

up at Barnum's Carnival Novelties. A good few years ago now.
It's perfectly clean ... (*He starts to put it on her.*)

DENISE (*anxiously to him*). What is it? I mean. I am a woman,
aren't I?

PETER. You have the body of a weak and feeble woman, but you
have the heart and stomach of a King and a King of England,
too!

DENISE (*depressed*). Don't tell me, I'm Henry the Eight ...

PETER. Elizabeth ...

DENISE. What?

PETER. You're Queen Elizabeth. Magnificent! (*He takes a ruff
out of the cricket bag.*)

DENISE. You carry this around with you – in a cricket bag?

PETER. Only for very special people. (*He is fastening the ruff on her.*)

DENISE. Have there been many of them?

PETER. What?

DENISE. Special people?

PETER. Never one who looked so absolutely right in the ruff.
You could have been made for it. (*He goes to the bag, gets out a
crown and puts it on her.*)

DENISE. I've always fancied myself in a crown ...

PETER. Oh, there's just this ...

DENISE. What ...

PETER. The sceptre. (*He gets it out of the bag and hands it to her.*)

DENISE. Did she carry it around with her always?

PETER. I like to think so.

She moves towards him regally.

Now say, I may have the body of a weak and feeble woman,
but I have the heart and stomach of a king.

DENISE. I may have the body of a weak and feeble woman, but
I have the heart and stomach of a king.

PETER (*very pleased*). I knew you'd pick it up quickly. The
moment I spotted you in the lift ... Here's the puddle ...
(*He points to the carpet down by the bed.*)

DENISE. Is it? (*She looks down at the carpet, suspicious.*)

PETER. Wet weather. Slops. Inadequate drains. A most objectionable green and stagnant patch, slap in the middle of your Royal Progress. You know, Bulstrode mentioned it quite casually. There was a puddle, he said, slap in the middle of her Royal Progress. Little did he know . . .

DENISE. Little did he know what?

PETER. That it's haunted me all my life . . .

DENISE. Oh, Peter.

He looks at her, delighted beyond his wildest dreams.

PETER. Now, am I to be spattered with foul mud all the way twixt here and Tilbury?

DENISE. Am I to be spattered with foul mud all the way twixt here and Tilbury?

PETER. Never, Your Majesty, never!

He whips off his cloak, kneels at her feet with the cloak spread on the ground. He is now kneeling downstage of the bed, she is standing in front of him, between the bed and the door.

(*Under his breath.*) Do you think you could possibly – spurn me with your foot?

Her foot is poised to give him a sharp kick when the bedroom door opens and ROY *comes in. He is dressed in a business suit, wears thick glasses and has a jolly, amiable chairside manner.*

ROY. Hi there, darling . . .

He walks across the bedroom and into the bathroom where he can be heard clattering with things on a glass shelf.

(*O.S.*) What's happened to the Alka Seltzer?

DENISE. Look in the cupboard.

She holds out her dress in a vain attempt to hide PETER *who first makes for the cupboard, and then creeps towards the door as* ROY *speaks from the bathroom.*

(*O.S.*) Oh, thanks.

Sound of tap running as he pours it on to the Alka Seltzer. Neither DENISE *nor* PETER *move.*

ROY. Bloody awful hangover. I just couldn't face another mouth. I told nurse Fisher I just had to come home and lie flat on my back . . . (*He comes into the bedroom carrying a fizzing glass of Alka Seltzer.*) Oh well – I suppose it's not every night of your life that you get promoted to a Master Elk . . . I say, darling, you do look most awfully smart.

DENISE. I think you know Peter Trilby . . .

PETER *at the door, is frozen into immobility* . . .

You met him at the Dental Association's do . . .

ROY *moves towards the bed.*

ROY *collapses on the bed, kicks off his shoes.*

ROY. Couldn't we get a bit of air in here. I'm stifling . . .

DENISE *goes to the windows and opens the curtains. Then she switches off the lights at the door.* PETER *makes as if to leave.*

PETER. Well . . . I suppose I'd better . . .

ROY. Don't mind me. Ouch. I'll just lie here and suffer.

He lies with his eyes closed. Pause. Broken when DENISE *takes control of the situation.*

DENISE. Peter took me out to lunch.

ROY. That was decent of you, Trilby.

PETER. It . . . It was a pleasure.

ROY. Denise finds it quiet out here in Mill Hill all day . . . She used to be my dental nurse, you know . . .

PETER. She was telling me.

ROY. Bloody good chairside manner. I always said, she had the sexiest way of saying 'Rinse'.

PETER. I really should be going . . .

ROY. Tell me, Trilby. As a matter of interest. Do you greet your patients like that?

PETER. Like what, exactly?

ROY (*lying with his eyes still closed*). Well, aren't you all tricked out in doublet and hose or something?

DENISE. No.

ROY. No?

DENISE. No, actually he's not. He's got a cloak and ruff combined and a sword, naturally, and a sort of rather attractive feathered hat.

PETER. That probably gave you the impression I was wearing doublet and hose.

ROY. What the hell's the cloak for?

PETER. The cloak? Ah. You noticed that ...

DENISE. That's his gimmick.

ROY. His what?

DENISE. He's an Elizabethan Dentist!

ROY. Oh. (*He opens his eyes, looks at him.*) Is that what you are?

DENISE. You've heard of Elizabethan restaurants, haven't you? Full of roast swan and syllabub ... And rushes on the floor ... Well. Peter's brought the idea into the surgery.

ROY. And I suppose he ties a brick round your sore tooth and lobs it out of the window ...

DENISE. All right, Roy. He's not an Elizabethan dentist.

ROY (*sits up on the bed*). Would it be impertinent to ask you what he is exactly?

DENISE. He's just a friend.

ROY. I mean it's not every day of the week you come home and find a member of the National Dental Association kneeling on your floor – in full Elizabethan rig – not to mention a kind of feathery bonnet ...

PETER (*put out*). Oh really. I'll take it off. (*He throws his hat on the bed.*)

DENISE. Oh, don't be an idiot, Roy. Anyone can see he's Sir Walter Raleigh.

ROY. I don't care if he's Attila the Hun. What the hell's he doing in my bedroom?

PETER (*steps up to* ROY, *pugnaciously*). Blundell!

ROY. Trilby!

PETER. I take exception to that!

ROY. You take exception.

PETER. I cannot and never have been and couldn't possibly be – Attila the Hun!

ROY. Oh, don't do that!

DENISE (*pacifying them*). Please . . . Please, both of you . . . Don't be so childish . . . The whole thing has a perfectly reasonable explanation. (*To* PETER.) Shall we tell him?

PETER (*very agitated*). Tell him, what?

DENISE. There's nothing else we can do but tell him . . .

PETER. Denise . . .!

DENISE (*to* ROY). You see it's all part of history . . .

PETER. Denise! My secret . . .

DENISE. It's absolutely no good, Peter. Your secret's not a secret any more. Roy. One hot afternoon.

PETER. I do beg you. It's not a thing to be discussed in public . . .

DENISE. It is now. One hot afternoon, no less a person than Queen Elizabeth . . .

ROY (*very excited*). She rang?

DENISE. What do you mean. Rang?

ROY. Prince Andrew needs a brace . . . ?

DENISE (*with great patience*). Queen Elizabeth the First.

ROY (*disappointed*). Oh . . .

DENISE. One hot afternoon she was walking . . . out walking and there was this huge green stagnant puddle. Impeding her . . .

ROY. Impeding her what?

DENISE. Her Royal Progress. So – she turned to one of her courtiers who happened to be that well-known and tremendously attractive figure, Sir Walter Raleigh . . .

PETER (*agonized*). It's my secret!

DENISE. I'm sorry, Peter, your secret's not a secret any more.

And she said . . . 'Am I to be spattered with foul mud all the way twixt here and Tilbury . . . ?'

PETER *reacts, his hand over his face and a slight shudder.*

ROY. I've heard that before . . .

DENISE. Of course you have. It's a great moment from the past. But I bet you don't know where it happened.

ROY. Where?

DENISE (*triumphantly*). Absolutely here! In Mill Hill . . .

ROY. Mill Hill?

DENISE. Well, near Mill Hill. The place is actually now . . . a small island in the middle of the Barnet by-pass. (*She turns to* PETER *for confirmation. To* ROY.) Which is why it's going to be the most spectacular scene in the entire Pageant.

ROY. In the what?

DENISE. The Pageant! 'Mill Hill – Past and Future' . . . starting with the cave men of Totteridge and ending with a mock moon shot from the golf club.

ROY (*doubtful*). Look here, Denise. Level with me, why don't you. What's all this in aid of?

DENISE (*without hesitation*). Oxfam.

ROY (*looks at both of them, still doubtful*). A . . . pageant . . . you say?

PETER. Yes. Certainly, it's a pageant. Isn't that what we say?

ROY. Who got this thing up?

DENISE. Locally.

ROY. What?

DENISE. It's been got up locally.

ROY. Church do, is it . . . ?

PETER. I don't think it's anything to do with the church.

ROY. The Mill Hill Operatic . . . ?

DENISE. No . . .

ROY. Not the Rotary?

DENISE. It's just something that's been thought up . . .

PETER. By a few like-minded people.

ROY (*to* DENISE). Well, where do you come in, Lady in Waiting?

DENISE *proudly touches her crown.*

(*Suddenly deeply impressed.*) You're never the Queen?

DENISE. Who else?

ROY. They chose you . . . !

DENISE. I was on the short list apparently and then – well the decision came through at lunchtime.

ROY. Darling! It's amazing. Trilby . . . isn't it amazing? Selected! My little Denise . . .

PETER. To me your little Denise has always been Queen Elizabeth.

ROY. Well, when she was my dental nurse the patients always commented, 'That dental nurse of yours, Mr Blundell, is pretty enough for show business'. But I honestly never thought . . . Good heaven's, when's the great night . . . ? We must invite all our friends to watch the two of you . . .

PETER. What?

ROY. When's it coming off . . . ?

DENISE. Never. If you keep bursting in just when we're warming up!

ROY (*to* PETER). I don't know why you couldn't have said what you were up to in the first place.

PETER. Denise wanted to surprise you.

ROY. Oh? (*He goes up to* PETER, *looks at him critically.*) Funny thing . . . ! I should've thought Sir Walter Raleigh was a rather better built man myself.

PETER (*hurt*). I don't suppose you have the slightest idea what he was like.

ROY. Oh, don't you . . . ?

PETER. As a matter of fact, he's a particularly private character.

ROY. Oh yes?

PETER. Not many people understand him really.

Pause. Then ROY *says suddenly.*

ROY. Let's see you do it!

PETER. What?

ROY. If you're so marvellous at being Sir Walter Raleigh, let's see you at it.

PETER (*deeply shocked*). At it!? You mean with your wife?

ROY. Well, of course with my wife. You don't go solo, do you?

PETER. No...

ROY. I don't quite see you putting down your cloak to no one in particular ... Come on then, let's see what Mill Hill's going to be treated to ... on the night!

PETER. You can't expect us to do it now. We haven't had any practice.

ROY. I can make allowances for it being a little rough around the edges.

He goes to the armchair, sits down on it. Applauds.

PETER. Look here, Blundell. We can't ... I mean, it's not exactly meant to be thrown open to the public.

ROY. Well, if you don't throw it open to the public you won't raise very much for Oxfam, will you ... ? Come on then, where's the puddle?

DENISE. Oh, we might as well show him. (*She stamps into the middle of the room and points with her sceptre.*) Here ... Raleigh.

ROY. Come on, Raleigh. She wants you.

He goes to the bed and gets the hat which he puts on, adjusts, and approaches DENISE *with appropriate servility.*

DENISE. Am I to be spattered with foul mud all the way twixt here and Tilbury?

PETER looks at ROY *with intense embarrassment and dislike.*

PETER sighs heavily, detaches the cloak from his shoulders and kneels, spreading it on the floor. DENISE *walks across it and then they both stand and look at* ROY, *waiting for his reaction.*

ROY. Is that it?

PETER. Yes!

ROY. Oh, very good! You were lovely, darling. (*To* PETER.) I thought you were bloody awful, Trilby, quite frankly. (*He prises himself out of the armchair and approaches* PETER.) Have you never had a holiday on the Costa Brava? Have you no experience of bull fighting? El Cordobes? (*He stoops and quickly picks up the cloak.*) The movement with the cape! Pure poetry. (*He makes a quick bull fighter's pass.*) Isn't this the moment to give the spectators a treat?

PETER. I told you we've had hardly any practice . . .

ROY. Poetry . . . (*He makes another quick pass with the cape.*) . . . in motion! (*He throws the cape round his shoulders and fastens it.*) Look, do you mind if I show you what I mean? (*He moves to* PETER *and begins to unfasten his sword belt.*)

PETER. Of course I mind . . .

ROY (*girding on* PETER'S *sword*). I'd like to give you an idea about the sword too. Now then . . . (*He has the sword on.*) Where's the puddle got to?

DENISE (*points again with her sceptre and then turns on* ROY *imperiously*). Sir Walter!

ROY. Your Majesty!

> ROY *takes off* PETER'S *hat, puts it on his own head, and then sweeps it off to bow low to* DENISE, *in an elegant attitude with his hand on the hilt of his sword, the sword making his cloak stick out at an angle behind him.* PETER *winces and turns away.*

DENISE. Am I to be spattered with foul mud all the way twixt here and Tilbury . . . ?

ROY. God forbid, Your Majesty. Not whilst there is a humble cloak . . . to your loyal servant's . . . (*He whips off the cloak. Makes an elaborate pass with it.*) humble back . . . (*He is on his knees in front of her.*)

PETER (*to* DENISE). He's overdoing it . . .

DENISE. I think he's rather good. (*To* ROY.) My thanks, Sir Walter! (*She steps on to the cloak.*)

ROY. Your Majesty's life-long – and most humble servant . . . what happens now?

DENISE. I spurn you with my dainty foot. (*She kicks him playfully.*)

ROY (*delighted, he rises and bows*). God Save Your Majesty! (*To* PETER.) You see, Trilby. You need to give it *heart*!

PETER (*with growing fury*). Really!

ROY. Let's face it, Trilby! You're just not cut out for a big demanding role like Raleigh.

PETER (*now furious*). You don't know what you're talking about!

ROY. Oh, don't I?

PETER. 'Give it heart!' All that cheap vulgar olé-ing about with the cloak! You've got hold of the wrong end of the stick, Blundell! And in my opinion, it's about time you faced the truth!

DENISE (*a desperate shout to prevent* PETER *confessing to* ROY.) Oh, my God!

PETER. What?

DENISE. It's Thursday . . .

PETER. } What about it?

ROY   } (*looking at his watch*). So it is . . .

DENISE. Gerald's oboe lesson . . .

ROY. His what?

DENISE (*urgently to* PETER). Roy and I grew up without the benefit of the oboe – something we always regretted. You've got your car outside, haven't you, Peter?

PETER. Why?

DENISE. Well, we can hardly go and fetch Gerald from St Paul's Junior Prep like this . . . There'd be titters on the playground. Please, Peter . . .

PETER. I'm damned if . . .

DENISE. Peter!

PETER. Yes?

DENISE (*moves towards him, and propels him, with a series of sharp pushes, towards the door*). Is this the spirit that thumped the Armada? (*Push.*) Colonized Virginia? (*Push.*) Harried the Low Countries? (*Push.*) Dumped down his velvet cloak for his Queen?

PETER (*reluctant*). Oh, all right. Anyway, this afternoon's obviously a total, hundred per cent fiasco. (*Very gloomy, to* ROY.) How do I spot young Gerald?

ROY. Ginger hair. Overweight . . . And a couple of missing percuspids . . .

DENISE (*gratefully to* PETER *out of the door*). God bless you . . . I knew we could rely on your loyalty!

PETER (*to* DENISE, *resentful*). I should've guessed it. Some women become impossible – the moment you put a crown on them. (*He goes, slams the door.*)

DENISE (*great sigh of relief*). I thought he'd never go . . .

ROY (*puzzled*). Is it really Thursday – Gerald's oboe?

DENISE (*casual*). Oh yes. Definitely Thursday . . .

ROY. What do you think he meant exactly – by the wrong end of the stick?

DENISE (*looks at him and says with great enthusiasm – and to change the subject*). It's magnificent!

ROY. What is?

DENISE. I've never actually seen you – in a cloak before.

ROY. Makes a change, does it?

DENISE. A wonderful change – and the feathery hat!

ROY (*smiles, pleased*). Sits well on me?

DENISE. Wonderfully well . . .

ROY *struts to the mirror, admires himself in the cloak.*

You know what . . .

ROY. What?

DENISE. I'd say you looked exactly like Sir Walter . . .

ROY (*a moment of doubt*). Without the glasses?

DENISE. Even with the glasses . . .

ROY (*draws his sword – makes a pass in the mirror*). Don't the trousers rather spoil the effect? How long've we got – I mean before he gets back with Gerald?

DENISE. I'd say – quite long enough . . .

ROY (*pleased*). Long enough, eh? I suppose he never told you how it went on . . . ?

DENISE. When . . . ?

ROY. After she'd crossed the puddle . . .

DENISE. I expect she was tremendously grateful . . .

ROY. Shower him with gifts, did she?

DENISE. I'd say – lavished gifts . . .

ROY. Your Gracious Majesty! What sort of gifts exactly?

They begin to dance round, hand in hand, in a stately minuet.

DENISE. Dubloons!

ROY. Pieces of eight!

DENISE. Rare spices . . . Golden goblets . . .

ROY. Cuts off the Indies . . .

They are standing still, looking at each other.

DENISE. And finally, rumour has it . . .

ROY. Has what?

DENISE. She made him free . . .

ROY. Free of what?

DENISE. Of her Royal Person . . .

He embraces her, gently lifts off her crown and throws it on the bed. Kisses her as the curtain falls . . .

Bermondsey

Characters

IRIS PURVIS

BOB PURVIS

PIP LESTER

ROSEMARY

Scene

The living room behind the bar in the Purvis' pub – The Cricketers, Bermondsey.

Time

Christmas Eve, after closing time.

The Purvis' living room, behind the bar of the 'Cricketers' in Bermondsey. Peeling three-piece suite, wallpaper with pattern of Windsor Castle, ashtrays and calendar advertising 'Take Courage'. Christmas decorations. In the centre of the room, a Christmas tree, trimmed. The presents are set round: boxes in gold paper, unexpectedly large and lush. Christmas drinks: large selection on a table. Upright piano with carol book on it, open. When the curtain rises, the stage is empty. Sound of voices, children being put to bed upstairs. A young girl, blonde, mini-skirted and carrying a tray with two children's mugs on it comes in from the kitchen. She looks calm, in control, unhurried when a voice calls at her from upstairs.

IRIS. Rosemary? . . . Rosemary?
ROSEMARY. Yes, Mrs Purvis?
IRIS (*calls from O.S.*). Got the kids' hot drinks, have you?
ROSEMARY. Just coming.
BOB (*ad lib – OFF*). Good night. Happy Christmas, etc.

> BOB PURVIS *walks in from the bar. He's big, handsome, about thirty-eight. His life in the pub is starting to make him overweight.*

ROSEMARY. Don't know what your wife thinks she is – Shah of bloody Persia.
BOB (*ignoring this*). Taking that up to the kids, are you?
ROSEMARY. When're you going to tell her, Bob?
BOB. After Christmas. I'll tell her after the holiday.
ROSEMARY. Boxing day. Promise you'll tell her . . . ? (*She starts to go upstairs.*)
BOB. Of course I promise. After the holiday.

> *She goes.*

PIP LESTER *comes in from the empty bar. He's thin, sharp featured, grey round the temples, rather high upper-class voice, pianist's hands and gestures, dressed with perpetual under-graduate untidiness. Shapeless grey trousers, tweed coat with leather patches, old khaki shirt, straying lock of hair, slightly loping walk. He looks after* ROSEMARY, *doubtful and suspicious.*

PIP. (*feeling his arm*) I'm out of practice, pulling beer handles.

BOB. Why not open the shampoo, boy? That's what you're used to.

PIP *moves to the drinks tables, opens champagne.*

PIP. Children gone to bed, have they?

BOB. Iris never gets them off till past closing time – not on Christ-mas Eve.

PIP. Care for a glass of the old shampoo? (*He pours himself a gin.*)

BOB. Go ahead. I'll stick to the Mother's Ruin. Shampoo gets my gut.

PIP (*the cockney phrase carefully mixed with the upper-class accent*). Iris likes a drop of the old shampoo. (*He pours a gin for* BOB.)

BOB. Yes, Iris likes it.

PIP. The kids look smashing.

He takes BOB *his gin, then he looks at the big boxes round the tree.*

I hope my presents'll be a success.

Noise from above.

BOB. Cheeky little buggers. They're playing up.

PIP (*pats wrapped presents*). One Junior road-scorcher two-wheel Fire-Fly for Ronnie – and a rather impertinent looking person called 'Miss Isobel' who brings up her own wind for Carol Anne.

BOB. You spoil them!

PIP. Nonsense. I'm spoiling myself. Trying to make up for what I've missed.

He goes back to the table – takes his champagne.

BOB. You've not missed a thing. Iris says she can't switch on Late Night Line Up but you're chatting away about Brahms, or whatever...

Pause.

PIP *drinks, looks at* BOB.

PIP. Bob?
BOB. Yes?
PIP. Do you know how long it's gone on?
BOB. Since I married Iris? I was trying to reckon the other day. Ronnie's just eleven...
PIP. No. I mean ... *it.*
BOB. Oh, 'it'. 'It's' what you're talking about.
PIP. Eighteen years!
BOB. You're joking!
PIP. Eighteen years exactly. Since we stood on that horrible Parade Ground ... With Dulcie Dubbin screaming her head off at us ...
BOB. Our camp Sergeant! (*Remembering, imitating shrill Sergeant's voice.*) 'When I says "Fix" – yer don't fix!'
PIP (*same imitation – not so good*). 'But when I says "Bayonets" – yer pops them off and yer whops them on!'
BOB. When we was on an exercise near this bloody great castle, and Dulcie says 'This here's the property of Lady Thaxted. Mind your fairy footprints on the turf, you clumsy bastards'. And you said – 'Sergeant – she's my mother, and she'd like you all to come in to Christmas dinner'.
PIP. My mother's splendid, in National emergencies. She spent the war preparing an icy calm welcome for the German Commandant who never turned up.
BOB. Bit of an anti-climax then, a peace time invasion of National Service yobs ...
PIP. That was the first time I ever played the piano to you.

Remember, when Mother got the other on to Animal Grab . . . ?

BOB. You dragged me off into the Music Room. I thought you'd never stop. I thought, how the shit do I ask him to belt up, and then we got started on the whisky and the Christmas Carols . . . Is that eighteen years, honestly . . . ? Well, I'll say this, Pip. You've done all right for yourself since then, boy.

PIP. Not really. You've had all the great events . . .

BOB (*sarcastic*). Oh, yes! We just live on excitement here in the Cricketers. Do you know what happened? Just in the last three months?

PIP. I haven't been down. Not since Iris' birthday.

BOB. Was that when you brought her – a bottle of pong from the both of us?

PIP. Giant-sized Balmain 'Jolie Madame'. With a joke card from you to put your name to . . .

BOB. You see! Things only happen when you call on us! Since then, well, since then . . . We had Iris' Mum for one God awful weekend. Carol Anne got a pain in her gut which let everyone down by not being appendicitis . . . And oh, young Rosemary came to help Iris out. Ex-National Service Corporal Robert Purvis – This is your bleeding existence . . .

He drinks . . . PIP *laughs, drinks to him.*

PIP (*a little anxious*). Yes. Well, about . . . Rosemary?

BOB. Iris needed someone to help out.

PIP. Did she?

BOB. She's not a bad young girl. Had some trouble at home. Of course, Iris has to show her everything.

PIP. I noticed that.

BOB. But we do a lot more trade since her mini-skirt erupted in the saloon . . . (*Pause. He goes on, more confidential.*) Also, she's set me thinking . . .

PIP (*laughs at him*). Sounds bad!

BOB. No! No, it's been so long since I got talking to anyone as young as that – I don't count the kids, of course.

PIP. Of course.

BOB. And she got me thinking. Well, I'm in a bit of a rut, here, quite frankly, Pip. I mean, it's no use waking up and finding you've missed the bus, is it?

PIP. What bus exactly?

He goes to the piano and starts to play 'The Holly and the Ivy'. He's playing standing up and sings. BOB moves and stands close to him. PIP plays.

BOB (*puts a hand on PIP's shoulder*). Wasn't that the bloody tune?

PIP. . . . Remember?

BOB. Your Mum brought up Scotch in a decanter. She shoved it on the piano.

PIP. You've got a retentive memory!

BOB. We got pissed out of our minds, and sung that bloody thing all the way back to barracks. You're right, boy. It's retentive all right.

PIP suddenly stops playing. The two men face each other, move closer – BOB's hand still on PIP's shoulder. PIP speaks very quietly.

PIP. It's only eighteen years.

At the same moment they lean forward and kiss each other on the mouth.

Sound of a door banging and IRIS' voice on the stairs.

IRIS (*O.S.*). Quiet now, kids. Or Santa's not going to come. Not ever.

The men move apart, not hurriedly. IRIS comes in. She's the perfect pub wife: sensible, still attractive, tired from an evening in the bar and putting the kids to bed. She hardly looks at the men, but goes to the tree and straightens the silver ornament on the top of it.

IRIS. Can't ever get that old fairy to stand upright.

c

BOB. Stuff a twig up her.

Pause. Sound of children upstairs.

IRIS (*hearing it*). That girl's useless with the kids.

PIP *pours a glass of champagne and brings it to her.*

PIP. Shampoo, love?

BOB (*casual*). Rosemary – still up there, is she?

IRIS. Putting her eyelashes on. Apparently there was an accident in the bar. She left her other pair in an empty glass, and Mrs Beasley poured in a port and lemon and drank them down.

BOB. Silly old fool . . .

PIP. How revolting!

IRIS. I said what do you want to take them off in the bar for anyway, and she said – they get so heavy. After a long evening. She doesn't care if our regular barmaid gets a hairy lining to her stomach.

BOB. She's all right. She had a bit of trouble at home.

IRIS. I said, I should think they do get heavy, I said, with all that fluttering you do. She's hopeless with the kids.

BOB. Ronnie likes her.

IRIS. Carol Anne can't stand the sight of her.

BOB. Well, then – Carol Anne's a woman, isn't she?

IRIS. She's six!

BOB. It doesn't matter she's six. She's still a woman, isn't she? She's jealous. That's all. She's jealous of a bit of mini-skirt.

IRIS. Is that what I am! Jealous of *her*.

BOB. I should rather think so. The way you're criticizing.

IRIS. It's just that she's meant to be helping me out.

BOB. Oh, for God's sake, girl. Where's the spirit of Christmas . . . ?

IRIS. Drunk up by you, I should imagine. You must've got through one bottle of Gordon's since we opened.

BOB. I've been working . . .

IRIS. What do you think I've been doing? And trailing round

after a girl who's got no more sense than to let our bar parlour
staff drink down parts of her anatomy . . .

BOB. Give it a rest, Iris. Pip's here.

IRIS. Of course. Pip's here. Pip's always here! Christmas,
birthdays. One of the family!

She empties her glass.

BOB. Well, be grateful. You're swigging down his shampoo.

IRIS. Oh, Pip understands. You understand how it is, don't you,
Pip?

PIP (*crosses to* IRIS. *Fills her glass again. Looks at* BOB.) Yes, dear.
Of course, I understand.

IRIS. And what do *you* think of Miss Mini-Skirt exactly, Pip?

BOB. She's just a young kid – that's got into a bit of trouble at
home . . .

IRIS. No. What do *you* think of her Pip?

PIP (*pauses. He's in difficulties, he answers with tact.*) Charming.
She's just not – my type exactly . . .

Crash from upstairs.

BOB. I'd better go up, before the kids commit murder.

He goes. IRIS *shrugs her shoulders.*

IRIS. What do we do now? Sit in suspense until she drops the
other eyelash?

She drops into a chair, kicks off her shoes. Drinks. PIP *comes
over and fills her glass.*

PIP. You're tired.

IRIS. Bloody fed up.

PIP *goes to the piano. Starts to play 'The Holly and the Ivy'
quietly through this dialogue.*

IRIS (*after a pause*). How's your mother?

PIP. Indestructible!

IRIS. Shouldn't you be with her at Christmas? Isn't that your place – in the Castle?

PIP. Rheumatism Towers . . .

IRIS. Doesn't she miss you?

PIP. She's happy as a sandboy. She's sitting in front of a roaring electric fire, wrapped in two cardigans, fur boots, and the sari they wove for her in Delhi, playing consequences with the local M.P. 'Malcolm Muggeridge met Diana Dors in the Sauna Bath at the Vatican and the consequence was . . .'

IRIS. Is that what they play . . . ?

PIP. My mother always loved paper games with politicians . . .

IRIS. Your old mum. She's certainly part of history. Something like the Bloody Tower. (*Long pause.*) Of course, I know really – why you want to come here.

He stops playing abruptly. Listens tense.

PIP. Why?

IRIS. You're a bit of a snob, aren't you?

PIP (*gets up, puzzled, offended, but relieved*). Me! A snob.

IRIS. Take a trip round the stately pubs of Jamaica Road. Pay your half-crown and catch a glimpse of the 'real people'.

PIP. Iris, that's not fair!

IRIS. Oh, I've seen you. When Carol Anne puts sauce on her bread, your eyes light up as if you'd had a personal invitation to watch the Duke of Edinburgh eat his cucumber sandwiches . . .

PIP. Iris, that's just not true!

IRIS. I know what you say about Bob – 'salt of the earth. No nonsense. Real true person.' I don't know what you thought you'd met. Jesus Christ, just because he'd never seen a pair of pyjamas till he did his National Service . . .

PIP. It's all of you. This family . . . In the world I live in, there's no real feeling of a family any more . . .

IRIS. That's a load of cobblers . . . You don't think we're more real, do you – just because we have to make do with an Anglia instead of an Aston Martin, and vinyl instead of wall to wall carpeting. Just because we go on holiday in Hayling Island instead of borrowing old Lucy So-and-so's bloody Greek island.

PIP. Personally – yes I do.

IRIS. Why?

PIP. You're tired . . .

IRIS. *Why?* Tell me why – what's so good about us you have to drive down here with champagne and Paris Perfume, and walking, talking, peeing dolls. Just as if you were the Three Wise Men and I was the blessed virgin.

PIP (*trying to explain*). It's because . . . Honestly, it's because you're simple.

IRIS. Thank you very much!

PIP. I mean, you don't make great demands on life . . .

IRIS (*she gets up, impatient and restless*). What? Can't you hear? Bob's shouting all the time to be the twenty-five-year-old millionaire owner of the fifty storey de luxe Happy-Home holiday hotel, Torquay. You don't think the poor fact he's thirty-eight, and the tenant of a small tied house in the Jamaica Road makes any difference to what he's demanding, do you?

PIP. What about you?

IRIS. Oh, what I'm asking for's much more ridiculous.

PIP. What?

Pause.

IRIS. Love.

Pause.

PIP. You've got so much.

IRIS. Have I?

PIP. You've got Bob and . . .

IRIS. Have I got him?

PIP. And the children . . .

IRIS. Is that what you care about?

PIP. My Godchildren? Yes. Yes, of course. I mean, they must be very satisfying.

IRIS. A couple of accidents! If you want to know the truth.

PIP. Iris. I always thought of you as a perfect mother . . .

IRIS. That's what perfect mothers get landed with. Accidents.

PIP. I'm afraid I don't know much about it.

IRIS. That's not an area of scientific knowledge that really appeals to you, is it?

PIP. Perhaps not.

IRIS. I bet your greatest nightmare's being stuck here one weekend when I suddenly gave birth, and you have to rush in with boiling water.

PIP. Look, Iris. I don't want to seem old-fashioned. But it's Christmas Eve. We've decorated the tree. The children are asleep upstairs, and I personally thought we should practise the carol for tomorrow . . .

He goes back to the piano, and standing plays a few bars of 'The Holly and the Ivy'.

IRIS. Kids! They don't need us. You know what I seem to hear those kids saying all the time? 'We're just an excuse for you, aren't we? All you need us for is to keep your mind off the real trouble.'

PIP (*stops playing again*). What's that? (*Pause.*) What's the real trouble?

IRIS. Naturally, it's Bob.

PIP. What's the matter with Bob?

IRIS. What's the matter with *you*? You know what's going on . . .

PIP. He just seems a bit restless.

IRIS. Restless! Look – (*She stands looking at him.*) You love him, don't you?

Long pause.

PIP. I've always been very fond of Bob.

IRIS (*impatient*). Why can't you tell the truth sometimes?

PIP. Well, I do love him – naturally. As a friend . . .

IRIS. Oh yes, like you love your Mum. Like you love me. Like you're going to put 'With loads of love from Uncle Pip' on Ronnie's two wheeler.

PIP. Well . . . Perhaps not exactly like that.

IRIS. How?

PIP. Well . . .

IRIS. Go on, say it. How?

PIP. Well, I suppose . . .

IRIS. Oh, for God's sake. Do me the credit!

PIP. What?

IRIS. I'm not a complete bloody idiot. I mean I've got some idea – what's going on. He's your boy friend, isn't he?

  PIP *does a dramatic gesture, his head in his hands.*

PIP. What do you mean exactly?

IRIS. I never know . . . quite how to describe it.

PIP. I'm sorry.

IRIS. Look. It seems perfectly natural to me. It's the people that don't fancy him, I can't understand.

PIP. I won't come again.

IRIS. You've got to.

PIP. I'll stay away.

IRIS. I don't think we could do without you.

PIP. What're you talking about?

IRIS. The way I look at it is – you've kept this family together.

PIP (*incredulously*). *I* have?

IRIS. You've kept Bob steady. (*Losing patience.*) Do you think I'd've had a peaceful home to bring up the children and a good husband and holidays, if Bob hadn't had you as well to keep him feeling young and handsome as a boy of twenty?

PIP (*pauses. He looks at her.*) When did you work it out?

IRIS. Oh, I've known ever since you first took us out. Remember you got seats for the Victoria Palace? You said 'May I say how greatly I admire your hat?'

PIP (*desperate, embarrassed*). Look, Iris, my car's outside. On second thoughts, Mother may be feeling a bit low this Christmas, and I really think I should . . . (*Turns on her anxious.*) How could you tell?

IRIS. You were so polite to me.

PIP. Just because I happened to appreciate your hat . . .

IRIS. Do you imagine any of the other men we'd known'd say 'I greatly admire your hat?' They'd pile beside me in the back of the Anglia and try for a quick grope any time Bob had his eye on the road.

She drinks.

PIP. What I can't understand is, why didn't you object before?

IRIS. Why should I object? I tell you. I knew what Bob was like. I chose him like that, didn't I?

PIP. And I don't make you jealous?

IRIS. You're not jealous of me, are you?

PIP (*thinking it over*). No. I'm grateful to you, for looking after him.

IRIS. Well, I think you make a nice day out for Bob like going to the dogs, but less expensive . . .

PIP. Thank you very much. But . . . Why suddenly . . . bring it up?

IRIS. Have some sense! Can't you see what's happening to Bob? . . . I thought you loved him?

PIP. You know that, apparently . . .

IRIS. But you don't, do you? He's just the little bit of rough trade you took in to show round the Castle.

PIP. Iris, please!

IRIS. All right. If you care about him, why don't you put up a bit of a fight then?

PIP. Against you?

IRIS. Against her.

PIP. Her?

IRIS. Little Miss Eyelashes.

PIP. You're jealous of her. I believe you're jealous.

IRIS. Of course, I'm bloody jealous.

PIP. Why?

IRIS. Because she's a woman. And because she's nothing to do with Bob. She's not part of him. She's all in his mind, like the girls he gets on the brewery calendar, unzipping their jeans on black leather sofas. It's all a great big dream, and they'll take on a pub they can't afford, and put on dinners she can't cook and get brewery bills they can't pay, and it wouldn't be one bottle a day – but two and a treble before breakfast and you've got to put a stop to it. You've got to break it up, Pip dear. Before that girl takes my husband off both of us.

PIP. How can I?

IRIS. Tell her! Tell her he's queer.

ROSEMARY. 'Night, 'night, Ronnie.

> PIP *is stunned by this suggestion, when* ROSEMARY *comes in downstairs. She's put on enormous eyelashes and she's changed her clothes. She's carrying the emptied children's mugs on the tray.*

ROSEMARY. I'm not butting in, am I, Mrs Purvis?

IRIS. Not if I can help it, dear. Everything all right up there, then?

ROSEMARY. Oh yes. Mr Purvis was telling the kids a story. It was a scream. Shall I rinse these out under the tap?

IRIS. That's very sweet of you, dear.

> ROSEMARY *goes.*

You see? In eleven years, he's never told those kids a bedtime story. It's got serious . . .

PIP. Bob wouldn't be thinking of – leaving home, would he?

IRIS. If he does, I don't see her having you down for the holidays. (*She looks at him.*) Of course, we could always spend our Christmases together. Just you and me and the kids.

PIP. Perhaps . . . You're right.

IRIS. She's got to be told ...

PIP. Then, shouldn't you tell her?

IRIS. She'd never believe me. I'm just the old jealous cow, that's all I am. You see that, don't you, Pip dear? She'd never believe me.

   BOB *comes down the stairs, his hair brushed neatly.*

BOB. Well, got that lot into bed at last.

IRIS. Including our little Rosemary?

BOB. Sorry, Pip, the kids were just that bit excited.

IRIS (*exasperated*). What did you do? Calm them down with the one about the poor girl who lost her eyelashes dancing with Prince Charming who whipped her out of the Public Bar and made her sweetheart of the Forces.

BOB. I'm sick and tired of that.

IRIS. What exactly?

BOB. You getting at me. That's all you do now. Just get at me.

PIP (*embarrassed*). Isn't this the time we always have our Irish coffee? Christmas Eve.

IRIS. She won't know how to do Irish coffee – not that plastic daffodil out there. Most she knows is how to open crisps.

PIP (*anxious to escape*). Shall I go and do it? Shall I go and do it?

IRIS. Why not. You could probably tell her quite a lot ... About the way we do things here.

   PIP *goes.*

IRIS (*to* BOB). You want to leave us, don't you?

BOB. I was going to tell you, after the holiday.

IRIS. Why not now?

BOB. I didn't want to spoil your Christmas.

IRIS (*seriously*). Thank you.

BOB (*collects himself for an outburst, and then explodes*). I want a different sort of place, that's all. By the river, where I could put on prawn cocktails, and charcoal grills and not just rest content with meat pies and cheese biscuits. Somewhere you could put

on a dinner dance – for the younger marrieds. I'm getting on,
Iris, I'm thirty bloody six. Well, don't I deserve it?

IRIS. You weren't thinking of including me? Not in the move?

BOB (*weak and apologetic*). I want a bit of something young around
me.

Pause.

IRIS. Thirty-eight.

BOB. What?

IRIS. You're thirty-eight.

BOB. You see, I'm not getting any younger.

IRIS. Neither am I.

BOB (*guilt making him angry*). Oh, don't try that. I can see that
coming. Bloody blackmail. So I've got to stay because I feel
sorry for you, is that it? You want me to pity you?

IRIS. No.

BOB. What?

IRIS. Have a bit of pity on yourself.

BOB. I'm no good. I know that.

IRIS. Yes, you are then.

BOB. What?

IRIS. Good. That's why we both love you.

BOB. You and Rosemary . . . ?

IRIS. No. You know I don't mean *that*. Me and Pip! We've got
good taste – both of us. We like you as you are. If you'd been
meant as the guv'ner of a dinner dance Country Club, that's
what you'd be by now.

The door opens. ROSEMARY *comes in; she looks extremely
puzzled.*

ROSEMARY. 'Ere, he wants the Irish Whiskey. Where is it, Bob?

BOB. Top shelf – up with the liqueurs and specials.

ROSEMARY. He says he's about to do miraculous things, with
cream and Irish Whiskey.

She goes off into the bar.

IRIS. It's too late, Bob. You can't go back and have it all different...

BOB. Keep me down! All right! Just keep me down all the time! Can't I have a bit of ambition?

IRIS. If anyone's achieved their ambitions I'd say it was you.

BOB. Gordon – Bennett! I've had less out of life than anyone.

IRIS. At a modest estimate. I'd say you've had – about twice as much.

> ROSEMARY *comes back from the bar carrying the Irish Whiskey. She speaks to* BOB, *nods towards the kitchen.*

ROSEMARY. Who is he, Bob?

BOB. Just an old friend, that's all.

ROSEMARY. He said you had a whole lot of laughs when you were in the army together. He called your Sergeant Dulcie Dubbin.

BOB. Old Pip – he'd come out with anything.

ROSEMARY. Do you like him at all?

BOB. Pip? I've known Pip for years.

ROSEMARY. I dunno – he seems funny to me.

> PIP *comes in with the coffee tray. Puts it down and takes the whiskey bottle from* ROSEMARY. *Speaks in a stage Irish accent.*

PIP. A little drop of something to lift us all into Christmas Day.

> *He starts pouring whiskey, and cream over a spoon.*

IRIS (*to* PIP). Bob's thinking of taking a new place.

PIP. I hope not. (*Pouring cream.*) I like it here best.

IRIS. Apparently he's fed up with S.E.16. He fancies a business more in the Thames Valley.

ROSEMARY. Or Marlow! Marlow's lovely.

IRIS (*to* PIP). He thinks he'll get a better class of young customer up there. He fancies facilities for dancing.

ROSEMARY. And a grill. Charcoal grill's nice.

IRIS (*to* PIP). And putting on dinners. With prawn cocktail.

Rosemary's got all the ideas. Bob thinks she's got a sharp little nose for business.

PIP (*suddenly positive*). I think it sounds revolting. Here you are, love. (*He hands her a cup.*)

BOB. What sounds revolting?

PIP. The Thames Valley. And the local Young Conservatives' annual do. Throwing bread rolls and gobbling down scampi and selections from Sound of Music and Pimms No. 1 and stripping off in Punts. (*He gives coffee to* ROSEMARY.) Coffee, love?

ROSEMARY (*angry*). I'm not your love.

IRIS. And overdrafts and dud cheques and ten barmaids – all with eyelashes.

PIP. I don't think that's the sort of place I would want to visit. (*He gives coffee to* BOB.)

BOB (*puzzled*). Thanks, Pip.

ROSEMARY. Well. No one's asking you.

Silence. BOB *and* IRIS *are looking at* ROSEMARY. PIP *goes to the piano stool. Sits on it quite still.* ROSEMARY *repeats, with extra courage.*

No one'll be asking you for Christmas. Not necessarily.

BOB *moves over to* PIP *as if to protect him: but he doesn't say anything. He puts his coffee down on the piano.*

PIP. No. I suppose they won't.

ROSEMARY. I mean, I'm not exactly sure. Are you the kids' uncle?

PIP. I'm just someone who comes for Christmas.

BOB (*protecting*). You'll be welcome, Pip, wherever . . .

ROSEMARY. Who is he? I'd like to know that first. Before we start extending invitations.

Puts down her coffee and moves towards PIP.

BOB. He's an old family friend, that's who he is, Rosemary.

ROSEMARY. Yes, I can tell he's old.

BOB. This'll interest you. His Mum inhabits a castle.

ROSEMARY. Well, why don't he go to her for Christmas?

PIP. It's a question everyone seems to be asking.

BOB. Because he always stays with me.

ROSEMARY. Always?

BOB. That's what I said.

ROSEMARY. Why – is he your long lost cousin, or something?

BOB. He's no relation.

ROSEMARY. Then who is he?

IRIS (*to* PIP). Why don't you tell her who you are?

> *But* PIP *ignores this. He looks at* BOB. *Lifts his hands to the piano and plays, singing.*

BOB (*to* PIP). Is that the one we're going to do?

PIP. We ought to start practising it.

BOB. How's it go?

PIP. The descant?

BOB. Yes. How's it go?

> PIP *plays the descant.* BOB *sings, looking at the sheet of music.*

ROSEMARY. What's going on?

IRIS (*as* PIP *goes on playing, she puts down her coffee*). It's a practice, Rosemary . . . It's gone on since the three of us got to know each other. It started for ourselves, really; although now we do it for the children. Christmas Night when we never open – we sing them a carol. And Mr Lester, that's Pip, him being musical, he insists on a practice and a proper performance. The kid's don't care much, quite frankly, but we enjoy it. (*She goes over to the piano, looks at the sheet of music. To* PIP.) Which is my verse?

IRIS (*sings*).

> The Holly bears a prickle
> As sharp as any thorn
> And Mary bore sweet Jesus Christ
> To be a Saviour.

ROSEMARY. I think it's bloody ridiculous!

PIP. Why? Bob's got a modest baritone and Iris might be described as a plucky soprano. It's not good, but it's not ridiculous.

ROSEMARY. I don't know why you don't open Christmas Day, and give a party, or have a dance or something for God's sake. Why just sit around singing hymns! I still don't know who he is. Anyway, I don't know why we need to have him every Christmas. (*To* BOB.) You're not married to the man, are you?

Long pause. IRIS *looks round.*

IRIS. I think it's time someone told her.

PIP (*looks back at* IRIS). Someone?

They both look at BOB; *he takes a deep breath.*

BOB. A long time ago. Eighteen years to be precise. Pip and I met as we was placed under the care of a maniac – Sergeant named by him 'Dulcie' – and we spent long, pointless days stamping on a dreary bit of parade ground near a dump called Bishop's Stortford. Well, one Christmas Eve a change came. Pip took me into his mother's house and played the piano in a high room with walls the colour of old birthday cake and we drank whiskey from a decanter while we got pissed bloody senseless. On the way home we climbed into a haystack that was all hard with frost, and we saw each other's breath in the moonlight. And suddenly, for no good reason, we grabbed each other like we were both drowning and proceeded to have it away as if all that side of life had just been invented. I regret to tell you, Rosemary, it didn't stop then. It's been going on ever since. So that's why Pip here's kept up with the family, and why he often brings the odd present at Christmas.

IRIS. Well, then. Now we all know.

ROSEMARY *has been listening with growing incredulity. At the end of the speech, she looks at the three of them grouped, silent, dignified round the piano. Her hand covers her mouth as if she's not sure whether to break into a scream or giggles. Then she turns and runs away through the kitchen. We can hear the back door slam after her, when everything is quiet.*

IRIS. We do this bit together, don't we?
PIP. Oh, yes.

PIP *plays. They all sing together.*

> The Holly and the Ivy
> When they are both full grown
> Of all the trees that are in the wood
> The Holly bears the crown.
>
> The rising of the sun
> And the running of the deer.
> The playing of the merry organ,
> Sweet singing in the choir.

Curtain

Gloucester Road

Characters

BUNNY THOMPSON

MIKE THOMPSON

TOBY DELGARDO

CLARE DOBSON

The action takes place in the living room of the Thompsons' maisonette in Gloucester Road.

Early Autumn.

Friday evening: the basement living room of the THOMPSONS' *Gloucester Road maisonette. It is a warm, cosy nest which they have made for themselves with old but still glowing wallpaper and Harrods' second-hand Jacobean type furniture in more or less disrepair, to which they have added some easy chairs. Red electric candle sticks with parchment shades on the walls. Somewhere a bunch of chrysanthemums in a cut glass vase. There are also relics of* MIKE THOMPSON'S *naval officer family. A big, dark Victorian painting of a remote ancestor in naval uniform. Among the pictures are photographs of George VI as an Admiral of the Fleet, a calendar of the Queen on Winston – Trooping the Colour, and prominent, a needlework picture, framed, of a ship at sea. Backstage centre, an archway shows the staircase which leads up to the ground floor on which their bedrooms and the front door are situated. Stage left there is a hatch in the wall which leads to the kitchen and beside it a door into the kitchen. Stage right there is a window through which the basement railings can be seen when it is daylight. However, as it is now dark, a red velvet curtain is drawn over it. Near to the hatch there is a dining table with chairs round it, a sideboard in the background, old bits of family silver on it. On the other side of the room, easy chairs round the telly. On a sideboard a record player and a pile of old seventy-eight records, together with a few long-playing musicals. Over it a large and smiling photograph of* BUNNY *as a Wren. Another, smaller, photograph of* MIKE *in naval uniform.*

Dinner is almost over. It has been taken on the dining table, on which there is an empty quart bottle of pale ale standing among the empty plates. BUNNY THOMPSON, *still very attractive, although it is some time since she left the W.R.N.S., is wearing trousers and a cardigan. Sitting opposite her at table is* TOBY DELGARDO. *He*

*is a second-hand salesman, ex-public schoolboy, in a suit and slightly
worn suède shoes, a small moustache and an R.A.F. tie.* BUNNY'S
husband, MIKE, *one time naval officer, now the manager of the
school uniform department in Pontings is, as the play opens, taking
a bottle of port out of a cupboard, holding it up to the light. When he
has satisfied himself that there is enough left in it, he goes to the
table and fills three thimble-sized glasses. Then he stands at the
head of the table and raises his glass.*

MIKE. The Queen!

BUNNY. Her Majesty! (*She drinks.*)

TOBY (*with a sigh*). God Bless Her – and all who sail in her! (*He
doesn't drink.*)

> MIKE *looks at* TOBY *with deep disapproval. They all sit down.*

MIKE. I resent that, Delgardo! While there's a drop of port in the
galley, the loyal toast will be drunk.

TOBY. At 109a Gloucester Road . . .

BUNNY. It's very nice, Mike. You do it very nicely . . .

TOBY. There's a good little wife speaking. (*To* MIKE.) Why don't
you weigh anchor one night and send this creaking old
maisonette sailing down Ken. High Street?

MIKE. Scoff on, Delgardo. Typical R.A.F.

BUNNY. Now then, you boys. No squabbling. (*She goes to the
sideboard, switches on an electric percolator and brings a tray
back to the table.*)

TOBY (*gets up with his glass, has a gulp of port, makes a wry face*).
What's this meant to be – port? Tastes like that Black Market
Communion plonk we used to buy in the Blitz – you'll be feed-
ing us whale steaks next!

> BUNNY *is clearing away the plates.*

MIKE. There's nothing wrong with a slice of whale. When your
back's to the wall.

BUNNY (*to* TOBY). Did you sell lots of cars today, Toby?

TOBY. None. But I got a free ride in a Rolls Silver Cloud . . . The clock was bloody deafening. Business is slowish.

MIKE. It's pretty slack in the school uniforms department at Pontings. (*Gloomy.*) And I can see what you're doing behind my back.

> TOBY *and* BUNNY *both laugh. As they laugh together* TOBY *puts his arm round* BUNNY'S *waist.*

BUNNY (*moving away from* TOBY'S *embrace as she goes on loading the tray*). Let me get on, Toby. We've got to get this done early.

TOBY (*helps her load the tray*). Why, angel cake? Why've we got to get it done early?

BUNNY (*moving with the full tray towards the kitchen door*). Because Miss Dobson's arriving. (*She goes out of the kitchen door.*)

TOBY. Oh, Miss Clare Dobson.

MIKE. Moving your quarters, are they?

TOBY (*during this speech he is collecting up pepper, salt, etc., which he takes to the hatch and puts on the ledge*). Has it escaped your notice, my dear Mike, that all my gear has been shifted into a kind of converted box room with a striking view of the back wall of the tube station?

> BUNNY *sticks her head through the hatch to collect the condiments.*

TOBY (*who is now by the hatch*). The bed's awfully narrow in there, Popsie. You won't mind, will you?

BUNNY (*smiles up at him*). I suppose I'll have to lump it.

> *They kiss each other through the hatch.*

MIKE. My God – you'll go too far one day, Bunny!

> BUNNY *immediately shuts the hatch and* TOBY *moves away from it towards* MIKE.

TOBY. Think, you old sea salt! Why ever do I put up with loyal toasts and draughts and firewood in the mattress and the original geyser out of H.M.S. Victory?

> BUNNY *comes in from the kitchen and crosses to the coffee percolator. As she passes* TOBY *he gives her a small slap on the bottom.*

Because I have this beautiful popsie on the kitchen floor every night when you're tucked up in bed reading 'Mr Midshipman Easy'.

BUNNY. Does it have to be the kitchen floor – what's wrong with the sofa?

MIKE. Will you stop leading him on, Bunny? Do you want to break up our marriage?

BUNNY (*to* MIKE). Do you, darling? (*Pours his coffee and moves with it to him.*) Coffee? (*She gives it to him and strokes the top of his head.*)

MIKE. You know they'd never have a divorced man in charge of school uniforms. It wouldn't do at all . . .

TOBY. You mean it'd put a kind of curse on all those long grey flannel shorts . . . ?

MIKE. There's a kind of sanctity which you wouldn't appreciate, Delgardo, in family life.

BUNNY. Anyway – we've got to stick together . . .

MIKE. I suppose so.

BUNNY. For the sake of the new lodger.

> *She pours coffee for* TOBY.

MIKE. Thank God it's female.

TOBY. Why, exactly? (*He picks up his coffee, drinks standing.*)

MIKE. Less temptation for Bunny. (*To* BUNNY.) That was the danger of the war for her, it was largely fought by men . . .

> BUNNY *sits down at the table. Pours her own coffee.*

BUNNY. You could take your pick – Admirals of the Fleet, white-haired five-starred Generals from Omaha, soft-spoken, Javanese War Correspondents . . .

TOBY. And yours truly ... (*He sits down beside her.*)

BUNNY (*looks at him, surprised*). Were you there ... Toby?

MIKE (*gets up, triumphant*). You see! She's got absolutely no recollection of you! You're a sort of soft grey blur in the background of her mind. (*He goes to the armchair. Picks up an evening paper to look up the TV programme.*) What did you tell us you were? Acting Lance Corporal in E.N.S.A.?

TOBY (*with pride*). I was actually one of the few.

MIKE. One of the few who stayed on the ground while the others went buzzing about in the air.

BUNNY (*to comfort TOBY*). Of course, I remember you, darling. (*She puts a hand on his arm.*)

TOBY (*eagerly*). The Renaissance Club, Cromwell Road – with tall green candles and a white piano ... ?

BUNNY. We went dancing there?

TOBY. And two lady policemen came and arrested you! You'd jumped your ship ...

BUNNY (*as if she remembered*). My ship – The Royal Naval Stores, Margate.

TOBY. They dragged you away from me. I was left beating helplessly on the doors of the Paddy wagon ...

BUNNY. Poor you! (*She puts her hand on the back of his neck, kisses him.*)

MIKE. In the name of God, Bunny! Can't you keep your fingers off him? Why can't you do something healthy, you two? (*He gets up to switch on the television.*)

TOBY. Like watching television?

MIKE. At least it keeps your mind off sex.

He goes to the drawer of the dresser, brings out a much thumbed pack of cards and old scorer. MIKE sits back to enjoy the television.

TOBY. Pontoon, Popsie?

BUNNY. All right, handsome.

TOBY goes back to sit with her at the table, deals out the cards.

TV. 'Battle of Britain Week! It's just twenty-nine years since a few knights on their cloudy charges jousted with the huge Nazi war machine and won the day!'

Sound of aeroplanes from the TV *and noise of rattling machine guns and bullets and whines.*

MIKE. At least there's something decent on the television tonight. I get so sick of all that violence . . . I can't recognize your face up there, Toby!

TOBY (*he gives her a card*). Bust?

BUNNY. No. Twist.

MIKE. I said, I can't recognize your face up there!

TOBY *gives* BUNNY *another card.*

BUNNY. Thank you, darling.

MIKE. It's revolting! Revolting!

As MIKE *is watching them, she kisses* TOBY *gently but firmly on the mouth. Miss* CLARE DOBSON *enters down the stairs. She has long hair, granny glasses and a small face. She is dressed in a bright coloured blanket and carries her belongings in a basket. She has many rings, and bells tinkle round her. She has an accent part Guildford (her home), part Liverpool, part American (her influences).*

CLARE. Someone must have left the front door open. I'm Clare . . . Do I detect an atmosphere of tension?

BUNNY *gets up and moves towards* CLARE.

BUNNY. Miss Dobson! Darling! Mike, this is Miss Clare Dobson . . . my husband.

MIKE *stands up.*

Miss Dobson's going to have the other room.

TOBY (*miserable*). I'm going to have the other room.

CLARE (*moving towards* MIKE). You're beautiful!

MIKE. Oh ... Am I really? (*He switches off the television.*)

BUNNY. And this is your fellow lodger, Mr Delgardo.

CLARE (*raises her hand to him*). Hail, fellow lodger! You're not quite so beautiful but I think you're good ...

TOBY. I won't be when you get to know me better. (*He moves eagerly towards her.*)

CLARE. What a stupid sort of thing to say. (*He is stopped in his tracks.*)

TOBY. Oh, was it ... ? Really I suppose it was.

BUNNY. .... I should've asked, you've had dinner, have you?

CLARE. I never eat dinner.

TOBY. You'll have to here – at the Captain's table.

She sits down in a yoga position with her basket on the floor. The two men both look at her and at BUNNY *in amazement.* TOBY *sits down under the shock.*

BUNNY. Perhaps you're tired ...

CLARE. No ... I don't sleep much. I like to sit on the floor and just rap away. I'm Clare. I'm a Saint.

Embarrassed pause. BUNNY *sits down too.*

TOBY (*helpfully*). I'm sorry, did you say you were Saint Clare?

CLARE. I don't know about her. I'm a Saint and I'm Clare. I'm not Saint Clare, not as has thus far been revealed to me.

Another awkward pause. MIKE *breaks it.*

MIKE. We've been listening to an excellent television programme – on the Battle of Britain.

CLARE. Battle of Britain – which one?

MIKE (*throws back his head and laughs*). What does that make you, Toby? Bonnie Prince Charlie or the Old Pretender?

TOBY. Never mind, my dear. I expect you think the sinking of the Ark Royal was some event in the Book of Genesis ...

CLARE. What book ... ?

BUNNY (*to* TOBY). He means the Bible ...

CLARE. Oh, the Bible. That really knocks me out, the Bible! (*She takes out a cigarette, lights it.*) There's a good potential feeling here . . . (*Frowns.*) The vibrations could be improved a little.

BUNNY. I'm sure you'd like to see your room now. (*Half gets up.*)

CLARE. Sit down! What's so urgent? We have all eternity before us. Maybe we could learn off each other.

BUNNY *sits down again.*

TOBY (*shuffling the cards*). I know a few card tricks.

CLARE. I don't mean that. You know what I think? I think it's a long time since you were all in contact with young people.

MIKE. Do you find us old, Miss Dobson?

TOBY. I don't seem particularly old to me . . .

MIKE. You mean you might get bored here, Miss Dobson, with no one of your own age?

TOBY (*sarcastic*). You could always take Miss Dobson out to the Round Pond – sail boats with her.

MIKE. We have a most amusing lodger.

CLARE (*enthusiastically*). Yeh. Sail boats. That'd be groovy!

Pause. TOBY *looks discomfited.* MIKE *pleased. He fumbles in his pocket. Brings out a pipe.*

MIKE. You see? You'll find it quite convenient here for Kensington Gardens. Mind if I smoke?

CLARE (*offers him a drag of her cigarette*). You're welcome. Have a drag.

MIKE. No . . . No, I'll stick to the old Navy mixture, thank you. (*He puts the pipe in his mouth.*)

CLARE. Do you call that smoking . . . (*Pause.*)

MIKE. You can still find a few quiet spots in Kensington Gardens.

CLARE. What're your wildest dreams?

BUNNY. What?

CLARE. I mean, let's face it . . . what do you really want out of life? Just let's ask that for a kick off.

TOBY. Want . . . ? (*Looks at* BUNNY, *puts a hand on her arm.*) A whole wet weekend in Brighton! With one particular friend . . .

MIKE. If you ask me your whole way of life is just a wet weekend in Brighton.

MIKE *disregards this. Long pause.* CLARE *asks* MIKE.

CLARE. What's yours?

MIKE. I've often wondered what it would be like to work in a lighthouse. Somewhere in the Outer Hebrides, where they only visit you at Christmas. It's not something one could expect one's family to share, of course.

Pause.

CLARE (*to* BUNNY). How about you?

BUNNY (*businesslike*). I don't know. I've never thought about it. As a matter of fact, I rather like it in the Gloucester Road. (*She gets up and moves until she is standing over* CLARE.) I've put your own soap and towel on the little table under the window. Will you be expecting friends in at all?

CLARE (*dreaming*). I want to have forty children by the forty most attractive men in the world . . .

BUNNY. Oh really – who are they?

CLARE. I've got a list, you know. (*She starts to burrow in her basket.*) Here . . . (*She hands* BUNNY *a crumpled list.*)

BUNNY (*reading aloud*). Ludwig Van Beethoven . . . William Shakespeare . . . Mahatma Ghandi . . .

TOBY (*puzzled*). Aren't some of these people dead . . . ?

BUNNY. Oh, I don't suppose that's going to stop her.

CLARE. No – you're right! Age makes no difference to me with a person. No difference at all. (*Pause.*) Have you ever been to Istanbul?

TOBY. Not . . . Not that I recall.

CLARE. It's great – Istanbul. You can just sit on the floor – and smoke and rap away – and ask questions . . .

BUNNY. I should think you could do that in Gloucester Road.

MIKE. Really, Bunny. That's hardly the point.

BUNNY. I'm sorry.

MIKE. The point is – it's the spirit of adventure.

TOBY. Oh, the Francis Chichester of S.W.7!

BUNNY (*firmly to* CLARE). I think I should explain to you about the geyser . . . You've got to turn the little handle on the left right out, and screw the tap on the other side away from you as far as it can go, and for God's sake face the wall when you light it!

MIKE. You'd better take Bunny's advice. She's used to explosions.

CLARE. Sounds kind of scary. O.K. then. You want to introduce me to the geyser? (*She gets up cheerfully.*)

BUNNY. Let me take your basket. (*She picks up* CLARE's *basket.*)

TOBY. I'll help you, Popsie!

MIKE. Stay where you are, Delgardo!

CLARE (*stands in the middle of the room, looking round at them all.*) There is tension here. We'll relax that tension. I feel the need – to give you all something.

Pause.

MIKE. What sort of thing, were you thinking of?

BUNNY *moves out of the stairs,* CLARE *follows her: she stands on the stairs, gives the V sign to the two men.*

CLARE. The message is peace. And what is the motto! The motto is enjoy!

She has gone up the stairs after BUNNY. TOBY *is left sitting at the table.* MIKE *goes to the sideboard and takes out a gas mask bag which contains his embroidery.*

MIKE (*he starts to embroider on a small tapestry frame*). I suppose you've got your sticky little eyes on her already.

TOBY. On who exactly?

MIKE. Our new lodger.

TOBY (*laughs*). Miss Clare Dobson? Not my cuppa quite frankly. I bet it's about as undulating as an ironing board under that long pink nightie. (*Stops laughing.*) Thank you very much. I rather prefer something to grab on to.

Pause. MIKE *sews.*

MIKE. Like Bunny?

TOBY. What?

MIKE. I said, like my wife?

TOBY. Oh, for God's sake get on with your knitting.

He gets up and goes and looks at the embroidered picture of a ship, extremely critically.

MIKE. It's not knitting as you know perfectly well. It's petit point.

TOBY. That ship took you three years to do.

MIKE. It's an art that calls for considerable qualities of character, and self discipline.

TOBY. It seems to be sinking, a sea of wool . . .

MIKE (*dignified*). I have depicted a storm.

TOBY. Looks like a sort of agitated cardigan.

MIKE. Petit point builds character. You should take it up. Keep your mind – off the other business.

TOBY (*turns on him*). Really?

MIKE (*sewing*). My old school chaplain used to tell us – how to deal with that. If ever you're troubled by feelings of tenderness, he used to say, for anyone in a lower form, get straight into a cold bath and say 'Down Satan'! (*Laughs.*) My God, Toby! You'd've spent your entire schooldays under water!

TOBY (*sullen, shuffling cards*). Bunny's hardly in the fourth form.

MIKE. Bunny, you'd better understand this, is a fundamentally decent chap.

TOBY (*outraged*). That's a filthy lie!

MIKE (*goes on, imperturbable*). Well brought up, with a few standards to her name.

TOBY (*laughing at him*). Innocent.

MIKE. . . . as one might expect from the only child of a naval officer.

TOBY. With the single exception of vicar's daughters. Those are the most voracious?

MIKE (*pitying*). Really, are you such an expert?

TOBY (*complacent*). A certain amount of water, has flowed under my bridge, old fellow.

MIKE. Oh yes? We hardly notice you slinking out at night, do we? – Or carrying a furtive breakfast for two up to your own room on Sundays.

TOBY. Why go out – when you can get it all at home?

MIKE. I'm not sure you are an expert anyway, on the subject of Bunny. Perhaps all you see of my wife, is the tip of the iceberg.

BUNNY *is coming down the stairs into the room.*

TOBY. Well, it's a pretty good tip, let me inform you.

BUNNY *strokes* TOBY's *hair as she sits down at the table to go on playing pontoon.*

BUNNY. Give us a card, sexy.

TOBY *deals to* BUNNY. MIKE *looks at them, shouts.*

MIKE. Do I have to have my home turned into a gambling casino.

TOBY (*sniffs*). Odd sort of smell, isn't there?

BUNNY. She's burning incense, in the bathroom. Mike?

MIKE. Yes?

BUNNY. I wonder what she meant by that . . .?

MIKE. What?

BUNNY. 'The message is peace.'

Quick fade to blackout.

The lights come up: autumn sunshine is streaming through the window and the open kitchen hatch. The curtains are drawn, it is about 12.30 on the Sunday morning. BUNNY's *hands put a tray through the hatch, on it are some assorted knives and forks and an elaborate sundae glass containing chocolate instant whip with a cherry on top, standing on a paper doily.* BUNNY *comes out of the kitchen. She has taken off her cardigan revealing a bright shirt underneath as she takes the tray from the hatch and carries it to the sideboard and puts it down. As she does this,* MIKE *comes downstairs wearing a tweed jacket and a dark blue silk scarf instead of a tie. He sees the chocolate whip and goes up to* BUNNY *his eyes blazing with anger. Grips her wrist.*

MIKE. Individual whip! In a glass! For him! It's the bloody favouritism! Putting my nose out of joint, all the time. Hot water bottles, top off the milk on his cornflakes, always save the wishbone and the nice bit of crackling for Toby! How I'm expected to put up with it – in my own home . . .

BUNNY. But you don't like chocolate whip. You prefer a hunk of Cheddar . . . !

MIKE. It's not that I'm talking about – (*He pushes her away from him.*)

BUNNY. It's just that I like to give him a treat, on Sundays when he comes home from the pub. He doesn't get much for lunch the rest of the week – only sandwiches . . .

MIKE. He can have sandwiches on Sunday too, as far as I'm concerned. Bread sandwiches . . .

BUNNY. You're jealous.

MIKE. Jealous! Of that (*Lost for words.*) . . . four letter man! That wet handshake with his co-respondent's shoes and a bit of Brillo pad stuck under his nose . . . Jealous . . . of Toby Delgardo! Don't make me laugh! (*Plumps down at the table.*)

BUNNY. You're not laughing.

MIKE. Yes I am. The idea's ridiculous!

BUNNY. Anyway, what's so marvellous about you?

MIKE (*proud*). I once had command – of a ship.

BUNNY. It was a small pre-fabricated Naval Stores – in Margate.

MIKE. That was a ship! As coming under the Lords of the Admiralty, she was classed as a ship . . .

BUNNY. Perhaps that's why (*She starts to laugh.*) it made me feel so seasick! (*She can't stop laughing.*)

MIKE. Shut up!

BUNNY. A seasick nissen hut. With you on the bridge . . . (*She stops laughing.*) Landlubber!

MIKE (*stands up, terribly affronted*). I said shut up! One more word out of you and you can get out of here – and take your precious boy friend with you . . .

BUNNY. You mean Toby?

MIKE. Of course I mean Toby.

BUNNY (*passionate*). At least Toby knows how to get a bit of fun out of life.

MIKE. Fun? You call that fun?

BUNNY. What do you mean exactly?

MIKE. Personally, I call it filth.

Pause.

BUNNY. You, Mike, if you don't mind me saying so, have a distinctly one-track mind.

MIKE. Me!

BUNNY. Obsessed with sex.

MIKE. You mean me?

BUNNY. A woman doesn't want sex day in and day out, Mike, even though that seems all you can contribute.

MIKE (*utterly astonished*). Aren't you rather speaking to the wrong fellow!

BUNNY. A woman needs something else . . . like a joke . . . or a bunch of chrysanthemums . . . or a turn on the floor occasionally.

MIKE (*deep contempt*). It wouldn't surprise me to learn that Toby Delgardo takes dancing lessons.

BUNNY. Well, why not? Just look at you! Size nine shoes that never learned to chassis. You can't even drink properly. (*She lifts an imaginary glass and says in a deep bass voice.*) 'Her Majesty, God Bless Her'. Shall I tell you something? I'm bored with Her Majesty ... I'd rather have a drop of gin ...

MIKE (*almost apopleptic*). That finishes it!

BUNNY. Good!

MIKE. That's the completely unchangeable final end!

BUNNY. Very good!

MIKE. Where're you going?

BUNNY (*picks up her handbag and grabs her jacket*). To see if someone'll offer me a gin and tonic. (*She shouts at him.*) With a slice of lemon!

> *She bangs out through the kitchen door. MIKE sits in the armchair. He picks up the 'Sunday Express', leans back in the chair and starts to read. CLARE comes down the stairs quickly.*

CLARE. Did I hear sounds of strife by any chance?

MIKE. What? Oh yes. A bit of strife going on. There usually is, on Sundays ...

> *She comes and kneels on the floor in front of him, gently pulling away the paper.*

CLARE. Come out. Come out from wherever you are.

MIKE. I was just – reading the paper.

CLARE. Be yourself then – shout.

MIKE (*he sounds tired as he puts away the paper*). It's exhausting sometimes.

CLARE. At home they didn't shout. She just hated him in silence.

MIKE. Your mother ... ?

CLARE. I remember sitting with her on top of a bus, we'd come up from Guildford for the day, and she held out her little fat pink hand to me – all glittering with gaudy jewellery. 'Remember when you're married, Clare', she said, 'always buy a joint two thirds of the size you write in the cash book.

E

Change the balance into precious stones, for when your old man bolts with the secretary'.

MIKE (*shocked*). You mean she was deceiving him – about the roast?

CLARE. She had untruthful vibrations. You look anguished?

MIKE. It's just that you were sitting on my foot. (*She moves.*) Go on about her.

CLARE. There were her awful finger joints, all encrusted with the cuts of beef he went without. I tell you, Mike, when I heard that, I got straight off the bus and left the country. We were just passing a railway station. Euston – yes. It was a 174 I imagine.

MIKE. Where did you go?

CLARE. The Caribbean.

MIKE. By train?

CLARE. In a ship! I think they said it was the Caribbean.

MIKE. Before the mast!

CLARE. No . . . (*Laughs.*) In the souvenir shop.

MIKE. You sold souvenirs?

CLARE. Ya, actually I gave them away. They put me ashore as soon as they found out . . .

MIKE. How ever did you get back home?

CLARE (*gestures with her thumb*). On the thumb.

MIKE (*admiring*). You've knocked about the world a bit?

CLARE. I don't know. I never think about it.

MIKE. I don't suppose in all your travels you've had any experience of life in the Navy?

CLARE. No, Mike. I don't believe I have.

MIKE. Neatness – that's the main thing about it. Just a couple of square foot to stow all your gear. The shirts . . . of course, have to be folded to a centimetre. And the shoes filled with well rolled socks and handkerchiefs – it's a small world, a person's locker in the Navy. It's all he needs.

CLARE. Ya, I travel pretty light myself.

MIKE. I imagine it's much the same thing in a lighthouse . . .

CLARE. You know what. We once lived in a lighthouse.

MIKE. You?

CLARE. Twenty-four of us. On the Island of Ischia.

MIKE. Oh, I'd want to be there alone. I mean . . . imagine of how it might be in the morning, making tea all by myself. Putting one blue and white cup and a shining spoon on the big wooden table. Sitting down to polish things. No one – all day to interfere with you. I sometimes think of packing my old ditty bag and . . . just . . . They must be quite short staffed, in the lighthouse industry. (*He looks at her.*) You made up your mind quickly, when you left your mother.

CLARE. Well, I couldn't stay with her, could I, not after she made that plastic remark?

> MIKE *gets up, disturbed at what she has told him, moves towards the sideboard.*

MIKE (*admiringly*). Decisive action! Straight off the bus into Euston station and out to the Caribbean.

CLARE. Well, it's no good kinda hanging about is it?

MIKE. I suppose not. (*Pause. He's still thinking it over. He looks at his watch.*) They'll be back from the pub, soon.

CLARE (*gets up, moves towards him*). Yes. I suppose they will.

MIKE. It's a funny thing. I was five years in the Navy and never left Margate. Your sea legs must be considerably better than mine! (*Pause.*) I wonder – where you'll land up?

CLARE (*shrugs, turns a little away from him*). I don't know really. I suppose . . . some day I'll have to go back to Guildford.

MIKE (*genuinely shocked*). What?

CLARE. See my family.

MIKE. You can't!

CLARE. Why?

MIKE. No. You mustn't do that. I mean you made up your mind. Remember. The spirit of adventure. Decisive action.

CLARE (*doubtful*). Ya, perhaps you're right.

MIKE. What did you tell us? – 'The motto is enjoy'.

CLARE (*looks at him, smiling*). You really groove it, don't you? (*She moves towards him, smiling.*)

MIKE (*tentative*). I suppose you've never thought of taking up life in a lighthouse.

> *She moves unexpectedly towards him and quickly kisses him on the mouth. They stand for a moment, looking at each other. Then he turns away from her towards the stairs.*

Thank you, Miss Dobson.

> *He runs quickly away up the stairs.* CLARE *shrugs, smiles to herself. There is a sound from the kitchen,* BUNNY *and* TOBY *coming in through the back door, home from the pub. They are singing together and their song goes on as they come into the room, arm in arm, still singing.*

TOBY and BUNNY (*singing*).
'She was sweet sixteen
On the village green
Always dancing on the village green'

> *They are in at the door. He is carrying pint bottles of Pale Ale in a string bag.*

'Pooer little Angeline . . . '

BUNNY. I've just had two large gin and tonics and two slices of lemon and the message is peace!

> CLARE *sits back on her heels and claps rhythmic.*

CLARE. Peace! Peace!

> *Sound of a timer ringing in the kitchen.*

BUNNY. My God. I must switch off the oven.

> *She picks up the bag of beer bottles and goes out to the kitchen.* TOBY *starts looking through the pile of records.*

CLARE. Do you turn each other on? (*She gets up and walks towards him.*)

TOBY. What?

CLARE. I mean – you know what I mean. Do you two make the most fantastic love together?

TOBY (*with difficulty*). Well. I mean we've – I've known old Bunny for a large number of years. We're the most terrific mates, of course. I mean, we're as close as two sticks . . . And speaking for myself . . . I must say I find her absolutely smashing! And you can keep your Betty Grable! (*He finds a long-playing record, takes it out of its sleeve and looks at it.*)

CLARE. Keep my who . . . ?

TOBY (*blows dust off the record*). She is just the most delicious popsie . . .

He puts the record on the turntable.

CLARE. But this afternoon – aren't you going to take her upstairs and make love to her till the stars fall out of her ears?

TOBY. Ssh!

BUNNY is coming back into the room drinking a glass of beer which she puts down on the sideboard as she squints at the gramophone turntable.

BUNNY. It's out tune . . . !

TOBY (*switching on the gramophone*). From the Rennaissance Club.

TOBY starts the record, 'Bewitched, Bothered and Bewildered'.

BUNNY. Is that where we heard it?

TOBY. Care for a dance, sailor? (*They start to dance together.*)

BUNNY. Mike hates dancing.

TOBY (*imitating* MIKE). I will not have my maisonette turned into a ten cent dance hall in Port Said . . .

CLARE. No, you dance. The whole world should dance . . . If you're filled with happiness, don't be afraid to show it . . .

BUNNY (*as she dances*). I don't think we're filled with happiness actually.

TOBY (*sings*).

'Couldn't sleep
and wouldn't sleep'.

BUNNY. 'When love came and told me I shouldn't sleep.'

> CLARE *goes up the stairs.* BUNNY *and* TOBY *are dancing as in a crowded night club, almost standing still.*

TOBY. This is the way I like dancing, plenty of contact.

> *He goes to the gramophone, starts the record again.*

BUNNY. You know, that girl's quite extraordinary . . .

TOBY. Miss Dobson?

BUNNY. I have to confess I looked in her basket.

TOBY. She talks sense in my opinion. As a matter of fact, she can see things perfectly clearly. I imagine they got born that way. It was probably the orange juice.

BUNNY. In Clare's basket there are two pairs of tights, three sticks of incense and a pot of Frank Cooper's Oxford Marmalade.

TOBY. Nothing else?

BUNNY. Absolutely, I swear, nothing else.

TOBY (*holding her tightly, stroking her bottom*). They miss such a lot when they dance nowadays. Capering about at arm's length.

BUNNY (*her eyes closed blissfully*). Chassis. Toby. Please, chassis.

TOBY. Let's hope to God no one comes to arrest you . . .

BUNNY (*she opens her eyes in wonder*). Is that true? Did it really happen?

TOBY. Shall I ever forget it? I was left beating on the dock gates as they took you on board in irons.

BUNNY. Sometimes, darling, you're inclined to exaggerate . . .

TOBY. Just when I'd got you . . . all lined up for the evening!

> *He suddenly kisses her seriously – a quite different kiss, an intent and serious pass, pulling open the buttons of her shirt, forcing her towards the sofa. There's a moment's struggle, she pushes him away. She looks at him, startled, horrified. He's helpless, puzzled.*

Why ever not?

BUNNY. I don't really think Mike would like it.

CLARE appears triumphant at the top of the stairs.

CLARE. Mike's gone. He took his kit bag. He had to see you . . . the motto is enjoy!

Quick fade to black out.

Lights up immediately and it is 8.30 a.m. on a sunny but autumnal Monday morning. MIKE *is sitting at the table which is half laid for breakfast, wearing his business suit and tie and reading the paper.* BUNNY *comes out of the kitchen carrying a tray with additional things including a pot of Oxford marmalade on it. She goes to the sideboard to unload the tray, looks at the Oxford marmalade and puts it beside the cornflakes and the full bottle of milk which are already on the table.*

She smiles at him. TOBY *comes clattering down the stairs combing his hair, tying his tie as he sits down and speaks as he fills his plate with cornflakes.*

TOBY. Hullo, Bunny. Good morning, Mike. What happened to you last night? Out on the town, eh?

MIKE (*with dignity*). As a matter of fact, I went to Euston Station.

TOBY. You old devil. What did you do there? Pick up Jamaican ticket collectors?

MIKE. There are other things to do at a railway terminus Toby, besides the relentless pursuit of sexual satisfaction. (*He looks at the table, sees that* BUNNY *has laid for three.*)

TOBY. Where's Saint Clare this morning?

BUNNY (*casual*). Oh, Miss Dobson? She's left us. (*She picks up the milk bottle, takes off the gold top.*) I told her I'd changed my mind about the room. It wasn't fair on you, Toby, disturbing you like that, after all the years you've been with us. (*She pours the top of the milk on to* TOBY's *cornflakes and then puts the bottle back on the table.*)

TOBY. Disturbing me?

BUNNY. Moving your room.

TOBY. I suppose the place was getting a little overcrowded.

BUNNY. She went quite quickly. She had very little packing. (*She moves to the kitchen door. As she gets there she turns to them.*) She left us her marmalade. How do you boys want your eggs?

MIKE. Fried.

TOBY. With fried bread.

> BUNNY *goes into the kitchen. There is a ring at the front door.*

MIKE. I'll get it. (*He goes up the stairs to the front door.*)

> TOBY, *humming 'Bewitched, Bothered and Bewildered' to himself, takes* MIKE'*s newspaper and starts to look at it.*

TOBY. By God – they've done it!

BUNNY (*O.S.*) Done what?

TOBY. They've captured the Albert Hall.

BUNNY (*O.S.*) Who?

TOBY. The squatters!

> MIKE *comes down the stairs again with a telegram, surprised.*

MIKE. It's a telegram.

TOBY. What?!

MIKE (*looks at it nervously*). We don't usually get telegrams.

TOBY. Who for?

MIKE. For all of us.

TOBY. Go on then, Skipper, read it.

MIKE. Sent from the all-night Post Office – Trafalgar Square . . . It's signed 'Clare'! 'I stopped a man for a lift on my way home to Guildford and as he was going to . . . to Afghanistan, I'm going with him. For the ride. P.S. I love you all three of you.' (*He takes the telegram over to the hatch and calls through it.*) Bunny! There's a telegram from Miss Dobson. Did you hear that? She loves us all . . .

BUNNY (*O.S.*) What?

MIKE. Miss Dobson says she loves all three of us.

BUNNY (*O.S.*) That's nice.

MIKE *folds the telegram carefully and puts it in his wallet. He goes and sits at the table opposite* TOBY *and fills his bowl with cornflakes.*

BUNNY (*calls O.S.*) You want fried bread too, Mike?

MIKE (*shouts back*). Were you thinking of leaving me out?

Pause. He puts sugar on his cornflakes.

TOBY. How was Euston Station?

MIKE. Changed, you know. (*Pause.*) They've rebuilt it considerably . . .

TOBY. It's a long time since I went there. (*He starts to eat cornflakes.*)

MIKE. They've taken away all the seats . . .

TOBY. What've they done?

MIKE. Removed all the seating accommodation. There's this great assembly hall – with flashing lights and train indicators and nowhere to sit down. Of course, I had my kit-bag with me . . .

TOBY. Did you . . . Why was that?

MIKE. I thought it might be needed.

TOBY. And was it?

MIKE. No. Not as it turned out. (*Pause.*) I'm glad you got your room back.

TOBY. So am I, actually.

MIKE. Besides which, the place was getting overcrowded.

TOBY. I felt that a little.

MIKE. She loves all three of us. (*He starts to laugh.* TOBY *laughs with him. Suddenly they both stop laughing as* MIKE *says.*) Delgardo?

TOBY. Yes?

MIKE (*lowers his voice*). Bunny told me something rather disturbing last night. We got to talking.

TOBY. Oh, did you?

MIKE. I thought I'd better let you know.

TOBY. Well, spit it out.

MIKE (*acutely embarrassed*). She said you'd never . . . I mean she told me that on no occasion had you two ever . . . actually . . .

TOBY (*he stops eating, looks hard at* MIKE). Come on – actually what?

MIKE. Well . . . gone the whole hog. (*Very worried.*) Can that be true? (*Long pause.* MIKE *looks at* TOBY, *worried.* TOBY *looks discomfited, sad, then cheers up as he says.*)

TOBY. Never trust a woman.

MIKE (*frowns*). What?

TOBY. You can't rely on a woman, not so far as the truth's concerned.

MIKE (*doubtful*). I suppose not . . .

TOBY. I mean, naturally she'd say that, wouldn't she?

MIKE (*cheering up*). I suppose she would.

TOBY. It doesn't necessarily mean that it's true though, does it?

MIKE (*spirits quite restored*). I take your point there! She might be pulling the wool . . .

TOBY. I'd say a whole fluffy blanket!

MIKE. Exactly! (*He picks up the milk bottle to pour milk on his cornflakes. Holding it he looks at it critically – then he yells at* BUNNY *in the kitchen.*) Bunny! You've done it again! You've given him the top off the milk! (*He crashes the milk bottle on the table.*) What do you think you're up to, Bunny? (*He gets up, moves to the service hatch.*) Flaunting it – under my very eyes. (*He shouts into the service hatch. He moves away, notices the record on the gramophone.*) And I see a record on the gramophone. I suppose you've been dancing together! (*He turns and shouts towards the hatch.*) If you think you're going to turn this place into a ten cent dance hall in Port Said I shall fight you in the streets, and I shall never surrender!

TOBY *is whistling 'Bewitched, Bothered and Bewildered' through this as*

The Curtain Falls.

Marble Arch

Characters

LAURA LOGAN

MCNEE

MISS PARKER

MAX

Place
Laura Logan's flat in Marble Arch Mansions, W.2.

Time
Friday morning.

LAURA LOGAN's *flat near Marble Arch. Lots of wrought-iron furniture, white furry rugs, white leather chairs. Centre – the bedroom. A big double bed unmade, dressing table, etc., white* TV. *Door left leads to a bathroom and a lavatory. We can see a part of the bathroom floor and wall behind the shut door. Door right leads to a hall into which the flat's front door, and kitchen and sitting-room doors open. A tallboy in the hall beside a hall table.* LAURA LOGAN – *one-time toast of the Rank Organization, Queen of Pinewood and star of a dozen forgotten British movies – is on the bed, red hair and pearls in place, wearing a flowing black negligee and doing her slimming exercises. On a chair by the bed, a man's dark jacket, waistcoat and tie. By the bed, an opened bottle of champagne and two glasses, a tray with coffee and toast for two, half eaten. Around the flat, photographs of* LAURA *in low cut dresses, riding habits, etc., signed pictures of James Mason, Stewart Granger, Patricia Roc and Margaret Lockwood. She stops exercising and shouts at the bathroom door.*

LAURA. Max! Max! (*She gets off the bed, pushes her feet into furry slippers.*) What's happened to you in there, Max? (*Shouts at the bathroom door.*) Don't you have to be back downstairs by ten-thirty? Hurry up for heaven's sake! Your lady wife'll be back from bridge with her Mother in Horsham, and all those sticky little drinks after dinner which stopped her driving back last night. (*She goes to the dressing table, starts brushing her hair.*) Do you realize if it hadn't been for the breathalyzer, I'd never have the full glory of a whole night in bed with you once a week, Max? And your filthy pipe in my Charles of the Ritz cleansing cream! (*Doing her eyes.*) For all these years – I only had you up to eleven-thirty Thursday evenings, and now – thanks to the inspiration of the Ministry of Transport, you can stay until Friday morning . . . Big deal! Big, enormous, sumptuous deal . . . (*She looks at the door curiously.*) Got a sudden attack of courage, or something? I mean, you're not going to run the risk of letting Phyllis find out, are you? (*Stops making up, talks to the door.*) Did I tell you, Max – I met your little Phyllis in the lift last week? Really, I hardly noticed her against the beige of the wallpaper . . . and she said 'Saw your old movie on the telly last night, Miss Logan . . . Amazing to see those movies now,' she said. 'Isn't it, Miss Logan?' (*She gets up, goes to the bathroom, shouts at it.*) Come on, Max! For God's sake – are you going to spend all day in my loo, contemplating . . . ?

She moves back to the dressing table.

I said 'No doubt movies always struck you as bloody amazing, particularly the arrival of talkies which must have come as something of a shock to you – late in life' . . . Don't worry, I didn't say that really . . . I mean, we couldn't say that to little Phyllis, could we? Phyllis has to be taken care of . . . (*She stands up and crosses to the champagne. Picks up the bottle and shakes it, her hand over the top, to restore the fizz.*) And what do I get? Six nights a week on my own, watching television. (*She picks up a glass.*) The Golden Years of the British Cinema! You won't even take me out to dinner. Oh no! We can't be seen together! All the portions of Israeli Melon and Coq au Vin and stuff en croûte you never dared buy me in public. Well, at least I made you pay for them, Max! One thousand and fifty-three dinners at the Mirabelle in cash. In shoe boxes under my bed! (*She stoops and pulls out a cardboard shoe box, opens it, showing it's full of five pound notes – gestures with it rudely at the door.*) Don't you think that's humiliating for me – having all my nights out in shoe boxes? You're a coward, Max! What's the good of you owning two film studios and thirty-three Orpheum Cinemas and Birmingham Weekend Television if you can't announce the take-over of a human person?

The phone rings beside the bed. She stuffs the shoe box back under it.

Who the hell's that? (*She pours herself another glass of champagne, drinks, picks up the phone and answers it in a purring actress's telephone voice, gentler and more former Rank charm school than the tones in which she has been abusing Max.*) Hullo? Yes. Yes, this is Miss Logan speaking ... (*She covers the mouthpiece and talks to the door.*) It's the B.B.C., Max. That's not one of yours is it? (*Uncovers mouthpiece.*) What? New Zealand Service? You want to what ... ? You mean they've just got around to seeing my films in New Zealand? Have they heard about the Battle of Alamein ... ? ... Oh yes. Well, of course you can interview me. Be delighted. From ten-thirty this morning I'll be free until next Thursday evening. (*She puts down the phone, says gloomily.*) It seems there's a good deal of interest in me, down under. (*She flops down on the bed drinking champagne.*) Interviews! It'll be quite like old times. I had a career once, remember? The day you first met me. Stage B at Shepperton, I was running down an iron staircase with nothing on but a few stuck-on sequins and an arse full of feathers. 'Mignonette ... Follies Girl and Heroine of the Resistance.' Well ... they really wanted Margaret Lockwood. They got her after that, didn't they darling? After you snatched me out of the public gaze, and stuck me in the flat above you and Phyllis so you could just creep up in the lift on Thursdays! Swine Max! (*She sits down on the edge of the bed, shouts at the closed door.*) If you'd ever had the decency to marry me ... I'd bloody well divorce you. (*She gets up, puts the glass on the bedside table, and walks up and down, furious.*) What's in it for me ... ? Sweating it out up here on massage and Easy Slim Biscuits so I can always be little feather-tailed Mignonette when I want to be your wife with a coat and skirt from Debenham's Outsize Department and twin beds where we could lie reading until we fell quietly asleep, and didn't care who knew it. I'm fed up with all this secrecy! Who do you think you are, anyway? It's like having it off with the Pope or something. (*She stands in front of the bathroom door. Shouts at it.*) I used to be young, Max. Can you hear me? I sat here on Monday, watching television. And there was I, a slip of a girl being raped by Stewart Granger, and I saw myself – all tear-stained with my lace jabot rudely torn away – and I said 'Cheer up, darling ... there's worse in store for you! Buried alive. That's what you're going to be. By the Chairman of the Board! Max! Max! (*Enraged, she beats on the door.*) Why can't you answer? What's the matter with you? Have you dropped dead in there?

She turns the handle and pushes the door violently. Greatly to her surprise, it is not locked. It opens. She goes into the bathroom and looks. She stands for a moment, looking in horror.

Oh, Max ... you have! (*Then she returns to the bedroom, shutting the door reverently. Long pause.*) Max ... my poor Max.

She goes to the bedside table, takes a cigarette out of a white alabaster box and lights it with her hand trembling. She sits down on the bed, facing the closed door, blowing out smoke. Long pause.

What do you think people are going to say ... ? (*Pause.*) I've got your reputation to think of. (*Pause.*) Oh, Max ... if you wanted to die, why couldn't you do it in your own flat?

There's a ring at the front doorbell.

Who's that?

The ring is repeated. She gets up slowly, looks despairingly at the bathroom door.

You'll get me thrown out of here, Max. Don't you know this place belongs to the Church Commissioners ... ?

The ring comes again. She moves out of the bedroom to the hall.

They even fuss if you get too noisy playing the Epilogue. Who is it?

MCNEE. It's me, Miss Logan.

LAURA. Oh, McNee...

She opens the door a crack. We can see a small segment of MCNEE, *the porter, standing at the door. He has gold-rimmed glasses, a severe expression and a Scots accent.*

MCNEE. I just brought up your things from the cleaner, Miss Logan.

LAURA. Thanks, McNee. I'll take it...

She opens the door a crack further, takes the cleaning, a couple of dresses on a hanger.

MCNEE. I'll be up in about five minutes for the rubbish, Miss Logan.

LAURA (*very nervous*). I... I haven't got any rubbish today, thank you very much. (*She goes into the bedroom, puts the cleaning on the bed.*)

MCNEE (*incredulous*). No rubbish?

LAURA. No rubbish at all... (*She shuts the bedroom door.*)

MCNEE. There must be rubbish in your tidy bin... Miss Logan. (*He pushes the door open and goes towards the kitchen.*) (*O.S. from kitchen.*) I'll be back directly.

LAURA, *who hasn't heard him, goes through the bedroom to the bathroom, turns away her head as she opens the bathroom door a crack, gets out the key from the inside of the door, and shuts the door again and locks it on the outside, leaving the key in the lock. She starts to move towards the telephone.*

LAURA. Who do I ring... Dr Fruteman? (*She sits on the bed, the telephone on her lap. Looks at it.*) Oh, Dr Fruteman... I think there's a man dead in my loo... (*She looks up at the bathroom door.*) Max... How could you! (*She starts to dial. As she does so,* MCNEE *comes out of the kitchen and crosses the hall.*

F

To the phone.) Oh . . . Is Dr Fruteman in, please? . . . You expect him any moment? Could you ask him to give me a ring? It's Miss Logan . . . Laura Logan. (*Annoyed.*) No, I won't spell it! It used to be a household word. (*She puts down the phone.*) If only Dr Fruteman could find you passed away peacefully . . . in your own bed, Max . . . (*She puts the phone back on the bed-side table. Moves towards the bathroom door and speaks at it.*) Don't you see, darling . . . it'd be so much more pleasant. (*She moves round the room.*) Well, it's only just downstairs . . . you'd only have to go down one floor to it. There's a lift . . . There's . . . a . . . (*An idea is dawning.*) . . . a lift! (*She goes to the door and speaks to it quickly, persuasively.*) It's just one floor, Max! But it'd make all the difference. All right?

No answer, so she answers herself.

All right . . . (*She moves quickly to the telephone.*) I'll need help, that's all. (*She looks at the telephone and then starts to dial.*) Is that Harrods? Oh, could you give me your Removal Department please? Removals! You undertake all sorts of removals? I don't mean of anything . . . I mean of anybody. Alive or dead . . . Well, I'm trying to explain. It's simply a question . . .

Front door bell rings.

Oh . . . I'll call you back. (*She slams down the telephone.*) It's always the same! Mend my own fuses – fix my own drinks . . . (*Speaks to the bathroom door.*) See what it's like, Max – being a woman on your own?

She goes through the bedroom door quickly, and shuts it behind her. She takes a deep breath, and opens the front door slowly. MCNEE *is standing there, with a rubbish disposal trolley. Two wheels and a long handle to which is fitted a large sack of reinforced paper, held open by a large circle of iron at the top and with a metal cover.*

MCNEE. Bring out your dead, Miss Logan!

LAURA. What? (*She moves back appalled as he walks past her. He stops to open the kitchen door. The rubbish disposal trolley between them.*)

MCNEE. It's my wee joke, Miss Logan. Something I often say, when I'm collecting the rubbish.

LAURA. Very . . . funny!

MCNEE. Sorry to keep ringing. I left my pass key downstairs.

LAURA. That's all right.

MCNEE. Not disturbing you, I hope . . . ?

LAURA. Oh, not at all really. (*As he gets the trolley.*) You've got a pass key, have you . . . ?

MCNEE. Downstairs . . .

LAURA. So you can get into any of the flats . . . ?

MCNEE. Oh yes. I have to. In case of accident . . .

LAURA. In case of accident! (*She looks at him hard.*) Mr McNee . . . You know the flat below here?

MCNEE. Number 4?

LAURA. Yes. Number 4 . . . Is the lady from Number 4 . . . back yet?

MCNEE. I don't think so. The car's not outside.

LAURA. I was just wondering . . .

MCNEE. Well, I'll just trundle this wee dustbin into your kitchen.

LAURA (looks at the dustbin, fingers it thoughtfully). It's not so wee, is it? . . .

MCNEE. What's not so wee?

LAURA. Your dustbin . . . ?

MCNEE. No . . .

LAURA. No. In fact, it's quite large. (*She opens the lid and looks into it.*) And empty.

MCNEE. I made you my first call . . .

LAURA. You could get . . . quite a lot of rubbish in there.

MCNEE. It's surprising.

LAURA. Strong, is it?

MCNEE. Double thickness, wet-reinforced, ten-ply wood-pulp paper, you'd be surprised the objects it's had in it . . .

LAURA. Would I . . . ?

MCNEE. As I often say, you can know a tenant by his rubbish . . .

LAURA. I suppose you can. Mr McNee. (*She grips his wrist.*)

MCNEE. Yes, Miss Logan?

LAURA. Please . . . (*She starts to pull him towards the bedroom door.*) Just come with me for a moment.

MCNEE. I've no got the time . . . The regulation is – all rubbish out of sight be ten-fifteen a.m.

LAURA. He's strict, isn't he?

MCNEE. Who?

LAURA. Our landlord. Who is it – the Archbishop of Canterbury? (*She has got to the bedroom door – opens it.*)

MCNEE (*as she gets him into the bedroom*). I'm told his Grace does keep a wee personal eye on the property.

LAURA (*she goes to the champagne bottle, shakes it to bring up the fizz*). And Marble Arch Mansions – was never touched by a breath of scandal.

MCNEE. Our reputation's untarnished.

LAURA. No suicides . . . no divorces. (*She pours out a glass of champagne for* MCNEE.) Have a drink . . . And no pets!

MCNEE. Not during the hours of duty. Pets are not allowed.

LAURA (*advancing on him with the glass*). But all the same, they're here, aren't they?

> *During the following dialogue she comes nearer and nearer to him, threateningly.*

MCNEE. What's here?

LAURA. Pets!

MCNEE. Pets? (*Shakes his head.*) Never! All animals forbidden, Miss Logan. (*He retreats from her, defensive.*)

LAURA. Only in theory, isn't that so?

MCNEE. It's my personal responsibility . . .

LAURA. In the night-time, I hear poodles coughing.

MCNEE. . . . to see there are no animals on the premises . . .

LAURA. I've seen turtles going up in the service lift . . .

MCNEE. Well, you have to turn a blind eye occasionally!

LAURA. Exactly! (*She pushes the glass into his hand.*) And how much does Mrs Montefiore pay you to keep quiet about her miniature Peruvian Apes?

MCNEE (*takes a quick drink from the glass of flat champagne*). It would be more than my job's worth.

LAURA. And what about the Guildersleeves in 6A?

MCNEE. What about them . . . ?

LAURA. If they're married, my name's Anna Neagle!

MCNEE. Some things are better taken at their face value, Miss Logan . . .

LAURA. And the two stockbrokers in Number 7!

MCNEE. Flatmates – From the landlord's point of view . . .

LAURA. And the sweet smell of Miss Cantor's cigarette is rare Egyptian tobacco, and those two married couples go into Number 9 every evening in full riding habit to play bridge.

MCNEE. You have to paper over the cracks once in a while, Miss Logan . . .

LAURA. Then paper over this one!

MCNEE. Which one?

LAURA. There's somebody dead in my bathroom.

MCNEE (*quickly empties his glass*). Somebody . . . ?

LAURA (*moves to the bed, gets the bottle of champagne*). Dead.

MCNEE (*looks at her disapprovingly*). Oo . . . Miss Logan, you haven't . . . ?

LAURA (*fills his glass*). Natural causes.

MCNEE. Is it someone you know?

LAURA. You know him too.

MCNEE. Who . . . ?

LAURA. The gentleman from Number 4.

MCNEE. But he's . . . a public figure . . .

LAURA. He has his private moments.

MCNEE (*lowers his voice*). You say he's passed over . . . ?

LAURA (*looks at the bathroom door, she speaks in a lowered voice also*). Yes.

MCNEE. In there . . . ?

LAURA. Yes.

MCNEE. But surely he's got a bathroom of his own . . . ?

LAURA. No doubt.

MCNEE. So what on earth . . . ?

LAURA (*suddenly aloud*). Oh, for heaven's sake, Mr McNee. You don't think he came up here just because he felt like snuffing out, do you?

MCNEE (*thoughtful*). No . . . I suppose he no did that . . .

LAURA. Life Peers don't seek this place out to die – like elephants!

MCNEE. Oo . . . Miss Logan. The landlords're no going to care for this . . .

LAURA. The landlords're no going to know.

MCNEE. It'll be in the papers . . .

LAURA. That he passed away in his own bed, while his wife was visiting her mother, and was found by their cleaning lady shortly before . . . eleven. That's when she arrives, isn't it?

MCNEE. What're you suggesting?

LAURA. Simply do your job, Mr McNee.

MCNEE. What job?

LAURA. Have the rubbish taken down. By ten-fifteen.

MCNEE. That's no a very nice way to refer to the gentleman.

LAURA. But that's what he is, at the moment. Don't you understand, Mr McNee? When you've taken him down to where he belongs, he'll be highly respected again. He'll be a force for good in the British Cinema, and the only Labour Peer to sell coloured television sets to Albania. And to me he'll be . . . well, he'll be how I always knew him. But at the moment – he's disposable.

MCNEE. I can't do it, Miss Logan.

LAURA. Are these service flats or aren't they?

MCNEE. Certain basic services – are provided.

LAURA. What could be more basic than this?

MCNEE. The Church Commissioners would nay like it . . .

LAURA. 'Lord Hammersmith found dead in wrong bathroom in

Marble Arch Mansions' splashed all over the Daily Sketch. How's that going to tickle the Church Commissioners?

MCNEE (*doubtful*). We've always done our best, Miss Logan, to make you comfortable at the Mansions . . .

LAURA. Did I ever give you a Christmas Box? I rather . . .

MCNEE. I'm sure . . .

LAURA. I'm sure I forgot. Here . . . (*She moves quickly to the bed, feels under it and pulls the cardboard shoe box. She takes out a handful of money.*)

MCNEE *looks at it, fascinated.*

Have some – of my dinner money!

MCNEE (*he holds out his hand, taking money*). I'm not sure . . . you didney forget Christmas . . .

LAURA. And your birthday! (*She puts more money into his hand.*)

MCNEE. Down the service lift? It might be possible . . .

He holds out his hand for more money.

She puts the lid on the shoe box and puts it on the bed.

LAURA. Final instalment – when the place is all tidy.

MCNEE. It'd be a comfort. To the poor widow.

LAURA. To us all . . .

MCNEE (*moves towards the bed*). I'll do it for you, Miss Logan.

LAURA. I'm sure you will. (*Moving between him and the shoe box. She puts the shoe box quickly under the dress from the cleaners.*)

MCNEE. I'll just slip down and get the pass key . . .

LAURA. Don't forget we haven't much time!

He goes quickly out of the bedroom and into the hall. He opens the front door of the flat and goes out hurriedly, failing to shut the door properly, so that it remains ajar. LAURA finds another cigarette, lights it. The telephone by the bed rings. At the same time the front door bell rings. She doesn't hear it. She picks up the telephone.

Yes . . . Yes, this is Miss Logan speaking. Oh, Dr Fruteman . . . how good of you to ring me back . . .

The front door is pushed open. A girl in a long footballer's scarf, wearing a duffle coat and carrying a tape recorder on a strap over her shoulder, comes in and looks round and curiously at the dustbin.

MISS PARKER. Hello, Miss Logan . . .

LAURA. Good-bye, Dr Fruteman.

MISS PARKER. I rang you from Bush House. Now, all ready for our little chinwag!

LAURA. Chinwag. I'm afraid that's out of the question now.

MISS PARKER. I'm thrilled to bits to meet you, Miss Logan. Is this your boudoir? Lovely. Listen, I wanted to take up the acting line myself. As a matter of fact I was singled out for praise by the Auckland Star for my Mr Rochester in the Jane Eyre of Charlotte Brontë. But when they ask me what I've done, and I say Mr Rochester at Auckland High, it doesn't help much towards getting those female roles I long for. Now, where shall we go?

LAURA. Nowhere!

MISS PARKER. Well, I had to come to London after all I'd heard about the sweet life in Earls Court, so I just bummed my way half round the world. It makes a fascinating story if you've got a moment.

LAURA. I haven't. Not a moment. I've got the workmen coming in. I'm having the place done over.

MISS PARKER. But you clearly said on the phone this morning . . .

LAURA. That was another lifetime.

MISS PARKER. Are you aware someone's left a dustbin deposited in your lobby?

LAURA. Yes. Well . . . how ridiculous.

MISS PARKER. It does create a somewhat ratty impression.

LAURA. That shouldn't be there.

MISS PARKER. Want me to move it for you?

LAURA. No ... No, I'll just put it in the kitchen ...

MISS PARKER *switches on her tape recorder and speaks into it.*

MISS PARKER. One-two-three-testing. (*Deep voice.*) I love you, Jane. Jane ... We are free my darling ... (*To tape recorder.*) My poor wife just burned to death in the west wing ... (*She puts down the microphone on the hall table by the tape recorder.*)

LAURA *comes out of the kitchen into the hall.*

LAURA. Miss Parker.

MISS PARKER. That looks better, doesn't it ... ?

LAURA. Look ... Miss Parker ...

MISS PARKER. I never get round to tidying my own place this early either. Every morning my flat mate and I swear to God we'll get things shipshape before we go to work, but can we ever ... ?

While MISS PARKER *and* LAURA *are speaking* MAX *crosses the strip of tiled floor and tries the bathroom door. He is a large man who looks stunned, having momentarily passed out on the loo. He's wearing a shirt with a wing collar only attached by a black collar stud and striped trousers with the braces hanging down. He tries the lock finding it locked and hearing* MISS PARKER's *voice from the hall and he retreats again out of sight. At the same time* LAURA *has got hold of* MISS PARKER *and starts to push her out of the flat.*

LAURA. I'll have to ask you to go, Miss Parker, the fact is, I'm not feeling well ...

MISS PARKER (*speaking at the same time*). Too bad ... you're feeling crook?

LAURA. The doctor's on his way up now, to give me a thorough check up. (*She is opening the front door.*)

MISS PARKER. Well, if you're not a hundred per cent ...

LAURA. I'm not. (*She has got* MISS PARKER *through the door and out into the corridor.*) Do ring me again. (*She starts to close the door on her.*) Fix up another appointment.

*She has the door closed. She leans on it for a moment, gives a
sigh of relief and goes into the bedroom, picks up the champagne
bottle, shakes it to make it bubble, pours out a quick glass and
looks at the clock.* MCNEE *opens the front door of the flat with
his pass key. Comes in, his pass key on a big ring in his hand and
looks for the trolley which he left in the hallway. Can't find it.*
LAURA *goes to the bathroom door : turns the key so that* MCNEE
can remove MAX. *As* MCNEE *reaches bedroom door, there is a
violent ring at the front door of the flat.* MCNEE *looks at it,
guilty and alarmed, not wanting to be found there on his curious
errand. He opens the kitchen door and goes quickly into it,
shutting it behind him.* LAURA *crosses the bedroom to answer the
front door. She comes into the hall and shuts the bedroom door
behind her. She opens the front door;* MISS PARKER *is standing
there.*

I thought I told you...

MISS PARKER. Steady on, Miss Logan. I left my infernal
machine!

*MAX appears again in the bathroom, still dazed and vaguely
hooking up his braces. He tries the bathroom door again, finds
it unlocked and emerges into the bedroom. He leaves the bathroom door open, puts on his coat and waistcoat, but leaves his
collar undone and forgets his tie. Then he tiptoes with elaborate
caution to the bedroom door, is halted by the sound of voices
still continuing and he stands with his hand on the bedroom door
handle, his ear against the door listening.* MISS PARKER *starts
to pack her tape recorder.*

They'd've slaughtered me back at Bush House if I'd left this
behind. Anyway, I'll need it for my next assignment. At this
very address as it happens ... I'm interviewing a tycoon of
considerable note...

Both LAURA and MAX react to this.

LAURA. A what?

MISS PARKER. Lord Hammersmith in person. I was booked for a chinwag with him and I thought as you lived in the same building and you still being such a name in Auckland . . .

LAURA (*appalled*). You're going down to Number 4 . . . ?

MISS PARKER. Right now.

LAURA. You can't do that . . .

MISS PARKER. Why not . . . ?

LAURA. Because . . . Because he won't speak to you . . .

MISS PARKER. Is he all that reserved?

LAURA. I've heard he's a very quiet man. Almost, totally silent.

MISS PARKER (*disappointed*). And I was hoping for a few tough words from him on the Sterling position – for the Dominions.

The kitchen door behind MISS PARKER's *head slowly opens, and* MCNEE *peers out. He gestures to* LAURA *pointing at his wrist watch. She nods and grabs* MISS PARKER *by the wrist, and drags her towards the sitting-room door. At the same time* MCNEE *closes the kitchen door.*

MISS PARKER. What was that?

LAURA. Just my cleaning lady. (*She takes her arm.*) Come in here with me. I'll give the Dominions something better than the sterling position.

MISS PARKER. Honest, Miss Logan?

LAURA. In the sitting-room. That suit you?

MISS PARKER. Too right! I promise you it'll be much appreciated.

LAURA (*opening the sitting-room door*). We won't be disturbed in here . . .

As LAURA *is moving* MISS PARKER *towards the sitting-room door which they are both facing.* MAX *opens the bedroom door a crack and peers out. Alarmed at seeing a strange woman in the flat, he retreats into the bedroom quickly. As he does so,* LAURA *gets* MISS PARKER *into the sitting-room.*

MISS PARKER (*on her way into the sitting-room*). How long can you give me, Miss Logan?

LAURA. Oh, just as long as it takes . . .

> *The sitting-room door shuts on them. This happens just at the same moment as* MAX *has shut the bedroom door. At the same moment,* MCNEE *opens the kitchen door and comes out. He looks round the hall, makes sure the coast is clear and goes back into the kitchen to fetch his trolley.* MAX *opens the door a little, sees the trolley being moved towards the bedroom and then moves back and hides behind the bedroom door just as* MCNEE *opens it, and tramps straight through the bedroom, into the bathroom with his trolley. As soon as* MCNEE *is in the bathroom,* MAX *whips out of the bedroom and into the hall. He looks into the hall mirror and sees his tie is missing – starts to go back into the bedroom when the sitting-room door opens.* MAX *moves to hide behind the tallboy in the hall. At the same time* MCNEE *moves, looking puzzled, into the visible part of the bathroom.*

MISS PARKER (*O.S.*) Miss Logan, if you don't mind, I'll just get some of your pearls of memory down on tape. Half a mo . . .

> MISS PARKER *comes quickly out of the sitting-room, grabs the tape recorder from the hall table, and is back again as* LAURA *appears at the sitting-room door. In the bathroom* MCNEE *is scratching his head.*

LAURA. Come back here . . . !

MISS PARKER. All set, Miss Logan!

LAURA. All right!

> MISS PARKER *goes into the sitting-room.* LAURA *shuts the sitting-room door on both of them. In the bathroom* MCNEE *shrugs his shoulders and starts to move his empty trolley out.* MAX *is emerging from behind the tallboy in the hall when* MCNEE *bangs the bathroom door shut behind him. At this moment* MAX *quickly opens the kitchen door and goes into the kitchen.* MCNEE

walks straight through the bedroom into the hall with his trolley. As he passes the sitting-room door, MCNEE *knocks on it and calls out.*

MCNEE. Your bathroom's all clear as far as I can see, Miss Logan.
LAURA *(O.S. calls from the sitting-room).* Thank you, Mr McNee . . . I'll speak to you later.
MCNEE. I'll be back directly . . .

MCNEE pushes his trolley out of the front door and bangs the door of the flat shut. MAX *then opens the kitchen door and comes out into the hall. He hurries back into the bedroom to get his tie, sees it hanging on the chair and starts to put it on leaving the bedroom door open. The sitting-room door opens and* LAURA *comes out, she looks round nervously.* MISS PARKER *comes out after her, her tape recorder slung round her shoulder, holding out the microphone to catch* LAURA'*s every word.*

LAURA. I'm sorry. My memory's rather short this morning. They'll have to make do with that.
MISS PARKER. I was hoping you might have a little more for your old fans, Miss Logan.

The bedroom door is open. MAX *retreats at the sound of* MISS PARKER'*s voice towards the bathroom.* LAURA *moves away from* MISS PARKER *towards the bedroom door.*

LAURA. Excuse me.

As LAURA *goes to the bedroom,* MAX *quietly shuts the bathroom door. He stands on the strip of tiled floor as* LAURA *comes into the bedroom followed by* MISS PARKER.

MISS PARKER. Perhaps we could get a bit further than your one trip to Hollywood.
LAURA *(looks round the room).* Forgive me! It's been a morning . . .
(She sits down, tired, on the edge of the bed.)

MISS PARKER comes close up to her, holding the microphone.

MAX puts his hand in his pocket, finds his pipe, takes it out and while he is waiting fills it from a tobacco pouch, sticks it in his mouth and finds a box of matches.

MISS PARKER. I'd like a scrap or two on the purely personal level. If you feel up to it.

LAURA. On the personal level?

MISS PARKER. Your name's never been coupled with any romantic attachment?

LAURA. Is that of any interest, to my fans down under?

In the bathroom MAX has got his pipe lit. He moves out of sight to throw the match down the loo.

MISS PARKER. Why, stone the crows, Miss Logan, I'd say of absorbing interest. Was there any particular male at all concerned.

LAURA. Any particular male?

In the bathroom MAX returns to view, blowing out smoke.

MISS PARKER. That made any deep impression on you?

LAURA. There was, now you ask me, one lasting relationship . . .

MISS PARKER kneels on the floor and holds the microphone out to LAURA.

MISS PARKER. Could you say it again, a little closer to the mike?

LAURA. I am issuing this statement to you, Miss Parker, on the strict understanding it goes no further than the other side of the world . . .

MISS PARKER. You were married once . . . ?

LAURA. Only on Thursdays.

MAX waits, anxious at what she is going to give away.

MISS PARKER. What? (*She holds the microphone closer to LAURA.*)

LAURA. He only had time for me once a week, although I had time for him always. But on a Thursday, when his family was otherwise occupied in Horsham, he would slip up here and make what can only be described as love . . . (*She pauses.*)

Still with his pipe in his mouth MAX *stoops down and listens, his ear to the keyhole, concerned, but also flattered at what he only half understands.*

MISS PARKER. Carry on, Miss Logan.

LAURA. He was the kindest man – and the most considerate lover. Love with him was like being handed gracefully into the warm, carpeted inside of a Daimler Hire. Our life together was not what might be considered exciting nowadays. I'd cook him roast lamb and rice pudding. His favourite programme was 'Come Dancing' and, more often than not, we'd be in bed before ten o'clock. But when we got there, it was extremely relaxed. There was a small vein in his forehead that pounded away when he read the 'Financial Times', and when I saw his head against the ribbons of my nightdress, that vein was quite still. He was an extremely clean man whose hands smelt of 'Wright's Coal Tar Soap'.

MISS PARKER. He sounds an almost perfect person . . .

LAURA. He had his weaknesses. Collecting – all manner of things. Old envelopes, bits of string, cotton reels, worn out rubber bands. He'd smooth out used brown paper and put it aside and say 'When the market falls this'll line my shoes on a wet evening'. He wouldn't go near the Embankment, on which he thought he'd end up sleeping.

MISS PARKER. What's happened to him now, Miss Logan?

LAURA. He's passed over.

MAX *is listening in extreme astonishment, takes out his pipe.*

MISS PARKER. Recently?

LAURA. It seems – some time ago now. Of course, I attended the funeral . . .

MAX *puts his still lit pipe into his jacket pocket as he hears this.*

MISS PARKER. Naturally ...

LAURA. Incognito. Being neither family nor business, I sat between his numerous relatives and innumerable employees like a stranger. I refused, with dignity, the invitation to attend the large chicken dinner with which his departure was celebrated.

MISS PARKER. My oath! It must have been a most moving occasion ...

LAURA. It was as he wanted it ...

> MAX's *pipe has begun to burn his jacket pocket and the clouds of smoke are increasing rapidly.*

LAURA. No fuss and no flowers. Simply the band of the Salvation Army playing selections from Rodgers and Hammerstein ...

> MCNEE *opens the front door with his pass key and comes into the hall, where he is stopped by the sound of voices from the bedroom.*

The Prime Minister was represented, and the urn was put where we always planned, with a view out all over Golders Green.

> *Suddenly* MAX *notices that he is on fire and starts to slap wildly at his pocket to put himself out.*

I hope he's happy where he is now. He always had a strong fear of foreign travel.

> LAURA *and* MISS PARKER *are silent. The front door opens,* MCNEE *comes into the hall.*

> MAX, *who has failed to put himself out, moves further into the bathroom out of our view, to get water.*

MCNEE. Miss Logan ...

> *Still wrapped in her golden memories of Max,* LAURA *doesn't answer him.*

> MCNEE *knocks on the bedroom door. The sound of his knock is*

drowned by the sudden rush of a tap and various crashes from the bathroom. MAX *backs into our view in the bathroom again, sloshing water from a tooth mug over his coat.*

At the same moment, MCNEE *opens the bedroom door – sees* LAURA.

MCNEE. Miss Logan, I came up to report to you that . . . (*Sees* MISS PARKER.)

LAURA (*looking amazed at the bathroom door.*) Whatever . . .

She turns and crosses the bedroom to pull open the bathroom door. MISS PARKER, *her tape machine slung around her, has risen to her feet and* MCNEE *is following* LAURA *to the bathroom door of which they both have a full view as* LAURA *pulls it open to reveal the soaked and extinguished* MAX. MAX *turns and smiles at them with a look of perfect calm and self-confidence.*

LAURA. Max!

MISS PARKER. Don't I recognize these famous features?

MCNEE. My lord! You are in the bathroom . . .

MAX. Good morning, McNee. 'Morning everyone.

MISS PARKER. Gee whiz. You wouldn't read about it. Is his lordship often to be found among your toilet facilities?

LAURA (*still amazed*). No . . .

MAX. No, of course not. I just popped up actually . . .

LAURA. You're alive . . . !

MAX. Alive? Of course I'm alive. It's not all that dangerous, you know. Fixing the plumbing. Gets you a bit on the wettish side, of course . . .

LAURA. Fixing the what?

MAX. I tell you, McNee, last night I hardly slept a wink! I was kept awake by the pipes up here gargling like the Hallelujah Chorus! So this morning, tired out and exhausted, I called up and asked if I might personally inspect my neighbour's ball-cock. It was pretty gruelling work, I might say actually. (*Starts to pull a gold watch out of his waistcoat pocket. Then speaks to*

LAURA, *with meaning.*) I must've snoozed off in there for forty winks. Didn't want to burst in when you had visitors . . . (*Looks at his watch.*) Good heavens! Is that the time? I must be trotting along. (*He moves towards the door.* MISS PARKER *is trotting after him like a small terrier.*) I think that's solved your little problem, Miss Logan. I don't think you'll have any more trouble with your pipes.

MISS PARKER (*running after* MAX). Lord Hammersmith, Oh Hoo Roo, Miss Logan. Lord Hammersmith! My Lord, what do you think of the Sterling position?

MAX. The sterling position? What position is that my dear? (*He pats her bottom jovially as they go out of the door together.*)

> MAX *and* MISS PARKER *are out through the front door.* LAURA *is standing in the centre of the bedroom. Then she picks the dress up, to put it away, reveals the shoe box.* MCNEE *looks at it, she looks at him.*

MCNEE. There you are, Miss Logan, things are n'ere so bad as they are painted. There's no need to explain, Miss Logan. We must just see that the landlord's asked no awkward questions.

> LAURA *gives* MCNEE £10.

Thank you, Miss Logan. I'll be up again tomorrow morning for your rubbish. As I often say – you can tell a tenant by her rubbish.

> LAURA *doesn't answer. He goes.*

> LAURA *is alone on the stage. She starts, listlessly to tidy up. Then she stops and sits on the bed. Slumped inert. She gets out a cigarette, lights it. Then immediately stubs it out in the bedside ashtray as the phone rings. She is on her feet, eyes blazing, angry.*

LAURA. Max! Where the hell are you phoning from? Your kitchen. Where's Phyllis – not back? And Miss Down Under, oh she's in the lounge, is she . . . Listen to me – you're a coward,

Max! A complete total one hundred per cent, terrified coward.
You couldn't even die up here, could you? That's what I've got
– a place you wouldn't be seen dead in. Wha . . . What're you
talking about? Of course I'm not the Board of Trade. Oh,
Phyllis has just walked in the room, has she? Well, why don't
you tell her, Max? Why not . . . ? You think I'm going to stay
up here . . . like a prisoner . . . always? Oh . . . Oh Phyllis
slipped out to the shops. What . . . what did you say? Oh, I
suppose so . . .

The anger goes out of her suddenly.

LAURA. All right, then. Yes, I'll be here . . . See you, Max.
Thursday as usual. See you . . . lover.

*She puts the phone down slowly. She picks up the stubbed-out
cigarette, relights it with her lighter – sighs and goes slowly back
to the routine of her everyday life. She goes into the bathroom.*

SOUND *of water as she turns on the bath.*

The Curtain Falls

Methuen's Modern Plays

EDITED BY JOHN CULLEN

*   *   *

Methuen Playscripts

*   *   *

Methuen's Theatre Classics